D1210114

A Concrete Approach to Abstract Algebra

A Series of Books in Mathematics

EDITORS:

R. A. ROSENBAUM

G. PHILIP JOHNSON

A Concrete Approach
to Abstract
Algebra

W. W. Sawyer

428 06

W. H. Freeman and Company

SAN FRANCISCO AND LONDON

The writing of this book, which was prepared while the author was teaching at the University of Illinois, as a member of the Academic Year Institute, 1957–1958, was supported in part by a grant from the National Science Foundation.

VANDERBILT UNIVERSITY
LIBRARY
NASHVILLE, TENNESSEE

© Copyright 1959 by W. H. Freeman and Company. The publisher reserves all rights to reproduce this book in whole or in part, with the exception of the right to use short quotations for review of the book.
Printed in the United States of America. Library of Congress Catalogue Card Number: 59-10215   (*c6*)

Contents

Introduction

The Aim of This Book
and How to Read It

AT THE PRESENT time there is a widespread desire, particularly among high school teachers and engineers, to know more about "modern mathematics." Institutes are provided to meet this desire, and this book was originally written for, and used by, such an institute. The chapters of this book were handed out as mimeographed notes to the students. There were no "lectures"; I did not in the classroom try to expound the same material again. These chapters *were* the "lectures." In the classroom we simply argued about this material. Questions were asked, obscure points were clarified.

In planning such a course, a professor must make a choice. His aim may be to produce a perfect mathematical work of art, having every axiom stated, every conclusion drawn with flawless logic, the whole syllabus covered. This sounds excellent, but in practice the result is often that the class does not have the faintest idea of what is going on. Certain axioms are stated. How are these axioms chosen? Why do we consider these axioms rather than others? What is the subject about? What is its purpose? If these questions are left unanswered, students feel frustrated. Even though they follow every individual deduction, they cannot think effectively about the subject. The framework is lacking; students do not know where the subject fits in, and this has a paralyzing effect on the mind.

On the other hand, the professor may choose familiar topics as a starting point. The students collect material, work problems, observe regularities, frame hypotheses, discover and prove theorems for themselves. The work may not proceed so quickly; all topics may not be covered; the final outline may be jagged. But the student knows what he is doing and where he is going; he is secure in his mastery of the subject, strengthened in confidence of himself. He has had the experience of discovering mathematics. He no longer thinks of mathematics as static dogma learned by rote. He sees mathematics as something growing and developing, mathematical concepts as something continually revised and enriched in the light of new knowledge. The course may have covered a very limited region, but it should leave the student ready to explore further on his own.

This second approach, proceeding from the familiar to the unfamiliar, is the method used in this book. Wherever possible, I have tried to show how modern higher algebra grows out of traditional elementary algebra. Even so, you may for a time experience some feeling of strangeness. This sense of strangeness will pass; there is nothing you can do about it; we all experience such feelings whenever we begin a new branch of mathematics. Nor is it surprising that such strangeness should be felt. The traditional high school syllabus—algebra, geometry, trigonometry—contains little or nothing discovered since the year 1650 A.D. Even if we bring in calculus and differential equations, the date 1750 A.D. covers most of that. Modern higher algebra was developed round about the years 1900 to 1930 A.D. Anyone who tries to learn modern algebra on the basis of traditional algebra faces some of the difficulties that Rip Van Winkle would have experienced, had his awakening been delayed until the twentieth century. Rip would only overcome that sense of strangeness by riding around in airplanes until he was quite blasé about the whole business.

Some comments on the plan of the book may be helpful. Chapter 1 is introductory and will not, I hope, prove difficult reading. Chapter 2 is rather a long one. In a book for professional mathematicians, the whole content of this chapter would fill only a few lines. I tried to spell out in detail just what those few lines would convey to a mathematician. Chapter 2 was the result. The chapter contains a solid block of rather formal calculations (pages 50–56). Psychologically, it seemed a pity to have such a block early in the book, but logically I did not see where else I could put it. I would advise you not to take these calculations too seriously at a first reading. The ideas are explained before the calculations begin. The calculations are there simply to show that the program can be carried through. At a first reading, you may like to take my word for this and skip pages 50–56. Later, when you have seen the trend of the whole book, you may return to these formal proofs. I would particularly emphasize that the later chapters do not in any way depend on the *details* of these calculations— only on the *results*.

The middle of the book is fairly plain sailing. You should be able to read these chapters fairly easily.

I am indebted to Professor Joseph Landin of the University of Illinois for the suggestion that the book should culminate with the proof that angles cannot be trisected by Euclidean means. This proof, in chapter 11, shows how modern algebraic concepts can be used to solve an ancient problem. This proof is a goal toward which the earlier chapters work.

I assume, if you are a reader of this book, that you are reasonably familiar with elementary algebra. One important result of elementary algebra seems not to be widely known. This is the remainder theorem. It states that when a polynomial $f(x)$ is divided by $x - a$, the remainder is $f(a)$. If you are not familiar with this theorem and its simple proof, it would be wise to review these, with the help of a text in traditional algebra.

Chapter 1

The Viewpoint of Abstract Algebra

THERE ARE two ways in which children do arithmetic
—by understanding and by rote. A good teacher, certainly in the earlier stages, aims at getting children to
understand what $5 - 2$ and 6×8 mean. Later, he
may drill them so that they will answer "48" to the
question "Eight sixes?" without having to draw eight
sets of six dots and count them.

Suppose a foreign child enters the class. This child
knows no arithmetic, and no English, but has a most
retentive memory. He listens to what goes on. He notices
that some questions are different from others. For instance, when the teacher makes the noise "What day is
it today?" the children may make the noise "Monday"
or "Tuesday" or "Wednesday" or "Thursday" or "Fri-
day." This question, he notices, has five different answers. There are also questions with two possible answers,
"Yes" and "No." For example, to the question "Have
you finished this sum?" sometimes one, sometimes the
other answer is given.

However, there are questions that always receive the
same answer. "Hi" receives the answer "Hi." "Twelve

twelves?" receives the answer "A hundred and forty-four"—or, at least, the teacher seems more satisfied when this response is given. Soon the foreign child might learn to make these responses, without realizing that "Hi" and "144" are in rather different categories.

Suppose that the foreign child comes to school after the children in his class have finished working with blocks and beads. He sees $12 \times 12 = 144$ written and hears it spoken, but is never present when 12 is related to the counting of twelve objects.

One cannot say that he understands arithmetic, but he may be top of the class when it comes to reciting the multiplication table. With an excellent memory, he may have complete mastery of formal, mechanical arithmetic.

We may thus separate two elements in arithmetic. (i) The formal element—this covers everything the foreign child can observe and learn. Formal arithmetic is arithmetic seen from the outside. (ii) The intuitive element—the understanding of arithmetic, its meaning, its connection with the actual world. This understanding we derive by being part of the actual universe, by experiencing life and seeing it from the inside.

For teaching, both elements of arithmetic are necessary. But there are certain activities for which the formal approach is helpful. In the formalist philosophy of mathematics, a kind of behaviorist view is taken. Instead of asking "How do mathematicians think?" the formalist philosophers ask "What do mathematicians do?" They look at mathematics from the outside: they see mathematicians writing on paper, and they seek rules or laws to describe how the mathematicians behave.

Formalist philosophy is hardly likely to provide a full picture of mathematics, but it does illuminate certain aspects of mathematics.

A practical application of formalism is the design of all kinds of calculating machines and automatic appli-

ances. A calculating machine is not expected to understand what 71 × 493 means, but it is expected to give
the right answer. A fire alarm is not expected to understand the danger to life and the damage to property
involved in a fire. It is expected to ring bells, to turn on
sprinklers, and so forth. There may even be some connection between the way these mechanisms operate and
the behavior of certain parts of the brain.

One might say that the abstract approach studies
what a machine *is*, without bothering about what it
is *for*.

Naturally, you may feel it is a waste of time to study
a mechanism that has no purpose. But the abstract approach does not imply that a system has no meaning
and no use; it merely implies that, for the moment, we
are studying the structure of the system, rather than its
purpose.

Structure and purpose are in fact two ways of classify-
ing things. In comparing a car and an airplane, you
would say that the propeller of an airplane corresponds
to the driving wheels of a car if you are thinking in terms
of purpose; you would however say that the propeller
corresponds to the cooling fan if you are thinking in
terms of structure.

Needless to say, a person familiar with all kinds of
mechanical structures—wheels, levers, pulleys, and so
on—can make use of that knowledge in inventing a
mechanism. In a really original invention, a structure
might be put to a purpose it had never served before.

Arithmetic Regarded as a Structure

Accordingly, we are going to look at arithmetic from
the viewpoint of the foreign student. We shall forget
that 12 is a number used for counting, and that + and
× have definite meanings. We shall see these things

purely as signs written on the keys of a machine.

Stimulus: 12 × 12.

Response: 144.

Our calculating machine would have the following visible parts:

    (i) A space where the first number is recorded.

    (ii) A space for the operations $+$, $\times$, $-$, $\div$.

    (iii) A space for the second number.

These constitute the input.

The output is the answer, a single number.

Playing around with our machine, we would soon observe certain things. Order is important with $\div$ and $-$. Thus $6 \div 2$ gives the answer 3, while $2 \div 6$ gives the answer $1/3$. But order is not important with $+$ and $\times$. Thus $3 + 4$ and $4 + 3$ both give 7; 3×4 and 4×3 both give 12.

We have the *commutative laws:* $a + b = b + a$, $a \times b = b \times a$. (Or $ab = ba$, with the usual convention of leaving out the multiplication sign.)

Commutativity is not something that could have been predicted in advance. Since $6 \div 2$ is not the same as $2 \div 6$, we could not say, for any sign S, that

$$a \text{ S } b = b \text{ S } a.$$

Some comment may be made here on the symbol S. In school algebra, letters usually stand for numbers. In what we are doing, letters stand for *things written on the keys of machines.* The form a S b covers, for example,

a "times" b,

a "plus" b,

a "minus" b,

a "over" b,

a "to the power" b,

a "-th root of" b,

a "-'s log to base" b,

as well as many more complicated ways of combining *a* and *b* that one could devise.

Commutativity, then, is something we may notice about a machine. It is one example of the kind of remark that can be made about a machine.

Ordinary arithmetic has one property that is inconvenient for machine purposes: it is infinite. If we make a calculating machine that goes up to 999,999 we are unable to work out, say, $999,999 + 999,999$ or $999,999 \times 999,999$ by following the ordinary rules for operating the machine.

We can consider a particular calculating machine that is very much simpler, and that avoids the trouble of infinity. This machine will answer any question appropriate to its system. It deals with a particular part or aspect of arithmetic.

If two even numbers are added together, the result is an even number. If an even number is added to an odd number, the result is odd. We may, in fact, write

$$\text{Even} + \text{Even} = \text{Even}$$
$$\text{Even} + \text{Odd} = \text{Odd}$$
$$\text{Odd} + \text{Odd} = \text{Even}.$$

Similarly, there are multiplication facts,

$$\text{Even} \times \text{Even} = \text{Even}$$
$$\text{Even} \times \text{Odd} = \text{Even}$$
$$\text{Odd} \times \text{Odd} = \text{Odd}.$$

Here we have a miniature arithmetic. There are only two elements in it, Even and Odd. Let us abbreviate, writing A for Even, B for Odd. Then

$$A + A = A \qquad A \times A = A$$
$$A + B = B \qquad A \times B = A$$
$$B + A = B \qquad B \times A = A$$
$$B + B = A \qquad B \times B = B$$

which may be written more compactly as

$$
\begin{array}{c|cc}
+ & A & B \\
\hline
A & A & B \\
B & B & A
\end{array}
\qquad
\begin{array}{c|cc}
\times & A & B \\
\hline
A & A & A \\
B & A & B
\end{array}
$$

Our foreign student would have no reason for regarding A and B in the tables above as any different from 0, 1, 2, 3, $\cdots$, in the ordinary addition and multiplication tables. He might think of it as "another arithmetic." He does not know anything about its meaning. What can he observe about its structure? Does it behave at all like ordinary arithmetic? In actual fact, the similarities are very great. I shall only mention a few of them at this stage.

Both addition and multiplication are commutative in the A, B arithmetic. For instance, $A + B = B + A$ and $A \times B = B \times A$.

In ordinary arithmetic the number zero occurs. We know the meaning of zero. But how could zero be identified by someone who only saw the structure of arithmetic? Quite easily, for there are two properties of zero that single it out. First, when zero is added to a number, it makes no difference. Second, whatever number zero is multiplied by, the result is always zero.

Thus

$$
x + 0 = x,
$$
$$
x \cdot 0 = 0.
$$

Is there a symbol in the A, B arithmetic that plays the role of zero? It makes a difference when B is added: $A + B$ is not A, nor is $B + B$ the same as B. A is the only possible candidate, and in fact A passes all the tests. When you add A, it makes no difference; when anything is multiplied by A, you get A.

Is there anything that corresponds to 1? The only distinguishing property I can think of for 1 is that multiplication by 1 has no visible effect:

$$x \cdot 1 = x.$$

In the A, B arithmetic, multiplication by B leaves any symbol unchanged. So B plays the part of 1.

This suggests that we might have done better to choose O (capital o) as a symbol instead of A and I as a symbol instead of B, because O looks like zero, and I looks rather like 1.

Our tables would then read

$$O + O = O \qquad\qquad O \times O = O$$
$$O + I = I \qquad\qquad O \times I = O$$
$$I + O = I \qquad\qquad I \times O = O$$
$$I + I = O \qquad\qquad I \times I = I$$

Now this looks very much like ordinary arithmetic. In fact, the only question that would be raised by somebody who thought I stood for 1 and O for zero would be, "Haven't you made a mistake in writing $I + I = O$?" All the other statements are exactly what you would expect from ordinary arithmetic.

The tables of this "arithmetic" are

		O	I
+	O	O	I
	I	I	O

		O	I
×	O	O	O
	I	O	I

We arrived at the tables above by considering even and odd numbers. But we could arrive at the same pattern without any mention of numbers.

Imagine the following situation. There is a narrow bridge with automatic signals. If a car approaches from either end, a signal "All clear—Proceed" is flashed on. But if cars approach from both ends, a warning signal

is flashed, and the car at, say, the north end is instructed
to withdraw.

In effect, the mechanism asks two questions: "Is a car
approaching from the south? Is one approaching from
the north?" The answers to these questions are the input,
the stimulus. The output, the response of the mechanism,
is to switch on an appropriate signal.

For the all-clear signal the scheme is as follows.

Should all-clear signal be flashed?

		Car from north?	
		No	Yes
Car from south?	No	No	Yes
	Yes	Yes	No

For the warning signal the scheme is as follows.

Should warning signal be flashed?

		Car from north?	
		No	Yes
Car from south?	No	No	No
	Yes	No	Yes

If you compare these tables with the earlier ones, you
will see that they are exactly the same in structure.
"No" replaces "O," "Yes" replaces "I"; "all clear" is
related to +, "warning signal" to ×.

One could also realize this pattern by simple electrical
circuits.

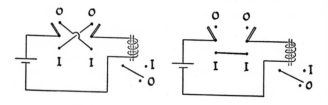

If you had this machine in front of you, you would not know whether it was intended for calculations with even and odd numbers, or for traffic control, or for some other purpose.

When the same pattern is embodied in two different systems, the systems are called *isomorphic*. In our example above, the traffic control system is isomorphic with the arithmetic of Even and Odd. The same machine does for both.

Isomorphism does not simply mean that there is some general resemblance between the two systems. It means that they have exactly the same pattern. Our example above shows this exact correspondence. Wherever "O" occurs in one system, "No" occurs in the other; wherever "I" occurs in one system, "Yes" occurs in the other.

The statements, "these two systems are isomorphic" and "there is an isomorphism between them," are two different ways of saying the same thing. To prove two systems isomorphic, you must demonstrate a correspondence between them, like the one in our example.

The study of structures has two things to offer us. First, the same structure may have many different realizations. By studying the single structure, we are simultaneously learning several different subjects.

Second, even though we have only one realization of our structure in mind, we may be able to simplify our proofs and clarify our understanding of the subject by treating it abstractly—that is to say, by leaving out details that merely complicate the picture and are not relevant to our purpose.

Our Results Considered Abstractly

So far we have been *concrete* in our approach. That is, we have been talking of things whose meaning we understand—numbers, Even and Odd, Yes and No. This is, of course, desirable from a teaching point of view, to avoid an unbearable sense of strangeness.

Now let us look at what we have found purely in terms of pattern, of structure, and without reference to any particular interpretation or application it may have. That is, we return strictly to the point of view of the foreign student. What can we say?

Well, first of all, we can recognize what belongs to the subject. Arithmetic deals with 0, 1, 2, 3, 4, 5, 6, 7, 8, 9. 7 is an element of arithmetic; "Hi" is not. "O" and "I" were elements used in our miniature arithmetic. "Yes" and "No" were elements in the traffic problem. The various positions of the switches were elements in the electrical mechanism.

So, first of all, our subject deals with a certain set of recognizable objects. Then we have a certain procedure with these objects. If we take the electrical machine marked $+$, and set the first switch to I, the second to O, the machine gives us the response I. We say $I + O$ is I. In the same way, if the teacher asks "3 + 4?" the children respond "7."

We may call adding and multiplying *operations*. A machine might be devised to do many other operations besides.

Thus in arithmetic we specify the objects 3, 4 and the operation "add" ($+$). The machine or the class gives us another object, 7, as a response.

We can list the things we noted earlier about arithmetic.

(1) Arithmetic deals with a certain set of objects.
(2) Given any two of these objects a, b, another object called their sum is uniquely defined. If c is the sum of a and b, we write $c = a + b$.

(3) In the same way a product k is defined. We write $k = a \times b$ or $k = a \cdot b$.

(4) $a + b$ and $b + a$ are the same object.

(5) $a \cdot b$ and $b \cdot a$ are the same object.

(6) There is an object 0 such that $a + 0 = a$ and $a \cdot 0 = 0$ for every a.

(7) There is an object 1 such that $a \cdot 1 = a$ for every a.

These are not all the things that could be said about arithmetic. We have not mentioned the associative laws, $(a + b) + c = a + (b + c)$, $a \cdot (b \cdot c) = (a \cdot b) \cdot c$; the distributive law, $a(x + y) = ax + ay$; nor anything about subtraction and division.

However, suppose we agree that statements (1) through (7) are enough to think about for the moment. We might ask, "Is ordinary arithmetic the only structure with these properties? If not, what is the smallest number of objects with which this structure can be realized?"

We already have the answer to both questions. Arithmetic is not the only structure satisfying statements (1) through (7). The smallest structure consists of the objects O, I with the tables for $+$ and $\times$ given earlier. (We are assuming that 0 and 1 are distinct objects.)

EXERCISES

1. Let O stand for "any number divisible by 3," I for "any number of the form $3n + 1$," and II for "any number of the form $3n + 2$." Can one say to what class $a + b$ will belong if one knows to what classes a and b belong? And the product ab? If so, form tables of addition and multiplication, as we did with the tables for Even and Odd. Do statements (1) through (7) apply to this topic?

2. The same as question 1, but with the classes O, I, II, III, IV for numbers of the forms $5n$, $5n + 1$, $5n + 2$, $5n + 3$, $5n + 4$.

3. Continue the inquiry for other numbers, 4, 6, 7, $\cdots$, replacing 3 and 5 of questions 1 and 2. Do you notice any differences between the results for different numbers?

4. An arithmetic is formed as follows. The only permitted objects are 0, 2, 4, 6, 8. When two numbers are added or multiplied, only the last digit is recorded. For example, in ordinary arithmetic $6 + 8 = 14$ with last digit 4. In *this* arithmetic $6 + 8 = 4$. Normally $4 \times 8 = 32$ with last digit 2. So here $4 \times 8 = 2$. Write out the addition and multiplication tables. Do statements (1) through (7) apply here? This arithmetic contains five objects, as did the arithmetic of question 2. Are the arithmetics isomorphic?

5. Calculate the powers of II, of III, and of IV in the arithmetic of question 2.

6. Are subtraction and division possible in the arithmetic of question 2? Do they have unique answers? What about the arithmetics you studied under question 3?

7. In the arithmetic of question 2, which numbers are perfect squares? Which numbers are prime? Does this arithmetic have any need of (i) negative numbers, (ii) fractions?

Two Arithmetics Compared

There is a certain stage in the learning of arithmetic at which the only operations known are addition, subtraction, multiplication, and division. The child has not yet met $\sqrt{2}$, but is familiar with whole numbers and fractions. I am not sure whether it would be so in current educational practice, but we shall suppose the child knows about negative numbers.

The charm of this stage of knowledge is that every question has an answer. You must not, of course, ask for division by zero, but, apart from this reasonable restriction, if you are given any two numbers you can add, subtract, multiply, or divide and reach a definite answer.

The body of numbers known to a child at this stage are referred to as the *rational numbers*. The rational numbers comprise all numbers of the form p/q, where p and q are whole numbers (positive or negative); p can also be zero but q must not. Since q can be 1, we have not excluded the whole numbers themselves.

The operations the child knows at this stage we may call the *rational operations*. A rational operation is anything that can be done by means of addition, subtraction, multiplication, and division, each used as often as you like. For instance,

$$\frac{(x+1)(y-\frac{1}{2})}{} + \frac{1}{3-\frac{2}{x}}$$

is the result of a rational operation on x and y. Note, however, that the process must *finish*. A child in grade school is not expected to cope with an expression like

$$1 + \cfrac{1}{2 + \cfrac{1}{2 + \cfrac{1}{2 + \cfrac{1}{2 + \cdots}}}}$$

and so on forever. This expression, in a certain sense, represents $\sqrt{2}$. The study of *unending processes* belongs to analysis: we exclude any such idea from algebra.

To sum up: There is a stage when a child sees arithmetic as consisting of rational operations on rational numbers. At this stage, every question has an answer, every calculation can be carried out.

Now we consider another arithmetic. On an island in

the Pacific, a sociological experiment is being performed.
A child goes to school and learns the addition and multiplication tables. This sounds quite normal. But the tables
he learns are the following.

+	0	1	2	3	4
0	0	1	2	3	4
1	1	2	3	4	0
2	2	3	4	0	1
3	3	4	0	1	2
4	4	0	1	2	3

×	0	1	2	3	4
0	0	0	0	0	0
1	0	1	2	3	4
2	0	2	4	1	3
3	0	3	1	4	2
4	0	4	3	2	1

You will recognize this arithmetic from a question in
the preceding section. 0, 1, 2, 3, 4 are the possible remainders on division by 5.

But the child has no such background. He is simply
taught the tables above. If he says $4 \times 2 = 3$, he is
rewarded. If he says 4×2 equals anything else, he is
punished. Now we compare arithmetic as experienced by
this child with ordinary arithmetic as learned by an
ordinary child.

To begin with, both children would accept the following statements.

(1) You can add any two numbers a and b, and there is
only one correct answer.

(2) You can multiply any two numbers a and b and there
is only one correct answer.

(3) $a + b = b + a$, for all numbers a, b.

(4) $ab = ba$, for all numbers a, b.

(5) $a + (b + c) = (a + b) + c$, for all numbers a, b, c.

(6) $a(bc) = (ab)c$, for all numbers a, b, c.

(7) $a(b + c) = ab + ac$, for all numbers a, b, c.

I do not know if the children would be able to prove
that all these were so, but at least they would be able
to take various particular cases, and admit they could
not find any instance in which any of these statements
was false.

Statement (5), for instance, in ordinary arithmetic, expresses the fact that when you are adding, say, the numbers 7, 11, and 13 it does not matter whether you argue

$$7 + 11 = 18, \quad \text{and} \quad 18 + 13 = 31$$

or

$$11 + 13 = 24, \quad \text{and} \quad 7 + 24 = 31.$$

The intermediate steps look quite different, but they lead to the same final result.

In the miniature arithmetic, an example would be adding 2, 3, and 4. You could either say

$$2 + 3 = 0, \quad \text{and} \quad 0 + 4 = 4$$

or

$$3 + 4 = 2, \quad \text{and} \quad 2 + 2 = 4,$$

the final answer being 4 either way.

Statement (6) expresses the fact that you can work out $7 \times 11 \times 13$, by writing

$$7 \times 11 = 77, \quad \text{and} \quad 77 \times 13 = 1,001$$

or equally well by writing

$$11 \times 13 = 143, \quad \text{and} \quad 7 \times 143 = 1,001.$$

Statement (7) expresses our experience that we can work out $4 \times (2 + 5)$ equally well as

$$4 \times 7 = 28$$

or as

$$4 \times 2 + 4 \times 5 = 8 + 20 = 28.$$

Corresponding procedures apply in the miniature arithmetic, though the results look strange to us.

If we had to work sums in the miniature arithmetic, there would be many of our habits that we could carry over and use to obtain correct results. In fact, statements (3) to (7) embody a very large part of the rules that we follow, consciously or unconsciously, in doing arithmetic or algebra.

Subtraction and Division

Our seven statements above make no mention of subtraction or division. When we learn arithmetic, $7 - 4$ is probably explained as "4 and what are 7?" This is, in everything except language, an invitation to solve the equation $4 + x = 7$. Further, grade school teachers have a strong prejudice to the effect that this equation has only one solution, $x = 3$.

The formal statement (8) below therefore contains nothing more than our own infant experiences.

(8) (i) For all a and b, the equation $a + x = b$ has a solution. (ii) The equation has only one solution. (iii) This solution is called $b - a$.

Here (i) and (ii) make statements that can be tested by taking particular numbers for a and b. Statement (iii) merely explains what we understand by the new symbol, $-$, that we have just brought in. It does not require testing or proof. It shows us, however, how to find, say, $2 - 3$ in the miniature arithmetic. $2 - 3$ is the number that satisfies $3 + x = 2$. In the addition table, we must look along the row opposite 3, until we find the number 2. We find it under 4, and only under 4. $3 + 4 = 2$, and no other number will do in place of 4. So $2 - 3 = 4$ is correct, and is the only correct answer.

Question: What does the requirement, that $a + x = b$ shall have one and only one solution for all a and b, tell us about the rows of the addition table?

When you subtract a number from itself, the answer is zero. We might express this in the statement: $a - a$ has a fixed value, independent of what a is; this value is called 0.

As $a - a = 0$ means the same thing as $a = a + 0$, we can equally well put this statement in the following form (that we have already met).

(*9*) There is a number 0 such that, for every a, $a + 0 = a$.

There can of course only be one such number; otherwise $a + x = a$ would have more than one solution, which would contradict part (ii) of statement (*8*).

Now we come to division. As children we meet division in much the same way as subtraction. "4 and what is 12?" is replaced by "4 times what is 12?" We might begin to write a statement, on the lines of (*8*), that $ax = b$ has a solution, and only one solution, whatever a and b. But this would overlook the fact that

$$0 \cdot x = 0$$

is satisfied by every number x, so that this equation has more than one solution, while

$$0 \cdot x = 1$$

is not satisfied by any number x.

Apart from this point, there is no difficulty in giving a formal statement of our experiences with division.

(*10*) For all a and b, provided however that a is not 0,
   (i) $ax = b$ has a solution. (ii) This equation has only one solution. (iii) The solution is called $b \div a$ or b/a.

Just as we can find $a - a$ to be 0 without knowing what number a is, we know in ordinary arithmetic that $a \div a$ or a/a is 1, without needing to know what a is, except of course that a is not 0.

So, as statement (*8*) was followed by (*9*), statement (*10*) is followed by (*11*).

(*11*) There is a number 1 such that, for every a, $a \cdot 1 = a$.

If you will now test statements (*8*), (*9*), (*10*), (*11*) for the miniature arithmetic, you will find that all of them work for it too.

This is quite remarkable. Within the set 0, 1, 2, 3, 4, without having to introduce any fresh numbers (like negative numbers or fractions in ordinary arithmetic), we can add, subtract, multiply, and divide to our heart's content.

For instance, in the miniature arithmetic, simplify

$$\frac{(\frac{1}{2} + \frac{2}{3}) \cdot (\frac{2}{3} - \frac{3}{4})}{\frac{3}{2} - \frac{3}{4}}.$$

We can get rid of the fractions in the numerator and denominator immediately:

$$\frac{1}{2} = 1 \div 2 = 3,$$
$$\frac{2}{3} = 2 \div 3 = 4,$$
$$\frac{3}{4} = 3 \div 4 = 2,$$
$$\frac{3}{2} = 3 \div 2 = 4.$$

The fraction is simplified to

$$\frac{(3 + 4) \cdot (4 - 2)}{4 - 2} = \frac{2 \cdot 2}{2} = 2.$$

There are many different ways in which this expression could be simplified. In the denominator, for instance, we could say $3/2 - 3/4 = 3/4$; and then division by $3/4$ is the same as multiplication by $4/3$. This would give

$$\frac{4}{3} \cdot (\frac{1}{2} + \frac{2}{3}) \cdot (\frac{2}{3} - \frac{3}{4}),$$

which can still be simplified in several ways. But however we proceed, we shall always arrive at the answer 2.

You may have noticed that $2 - 3 = 4$, $3 \div 2 = 4$. This shows that, for $x = 2$, $x - 3 = 3/x$. Are there any other solutions of this equation? We have

$$x - 3 = \frac{3}{x}.$$

Multiply by x:

$$x^2 - 3x = 3.$$

Subtract 3. Since $0 - 3 = 2$, this gives

$$x^2 - 3x + 2 = 0.$$
$$\therefore (x - 1)(x - 2) = 0.$$

So $x = 1$ and $x = 2$ are solutions. Could there be any more solutions? To show there are not we need to observe (12).

(12) $ab = 0$ only if $a = 0$ or $b = 0$. In words, a product is zero only if a factor is zero.

Above we had $(x - 1)(x - 2) = 0$. Either

$$x - 1 = 0 \quad \text{or} \quad x - 2 = 0;$$
$$x = 1 \quad\quad \text{or} \quad x = 2.$$

Thus quadratics can be solved by factoring exactly as in ordinary arithmetic. They can also be solved by completing the square. For example, consider

$$x^2 + x = 2.$$

To complete the square for $x^2 + ax$, we add $(a/2)^2$ to each side. In our equation $a = 1$, so $a/2 = 3$, since $2 \times 3 = 1$. We must add to each side 3^2, that is, 4. Thus

$$x^2 + x + 3^2 = 2 + 4 = 1,$$
$$(x + 3)^2 = 1.$$

Next we have to take the square root. $1^2 = 1$ and also $4^2 = 1$. (Note that $4 = 0 - 1$, so that ± 1 is the same as 1 or 4.) Thus

$$x + 3 = 1 \quad \text{or} \quad x + 3 = 4;$$
$$x = 3 \quad \text{or} \quad x = 1.$$

One can test by substituting these values in the original equation that they actually are roots.

This arithmetic will be referred to as "the arithmetic modulo 5." The number 5 in this title indicates that we are dealing with 0, 1, 2, 3, 4, the possible remainders on division by 5.

In the same way, the arithmetic of Even and Odd, with elements 0, 1 is called "arithmetic modulo 2." (On division by 2, an even number leaves remainder 0, an odd number 1.)

In earlier exercises, you were invited to study the arithmetics modulo 3, modulo 4, modulo 6, modulo 7, and so on.

EXERCISES

1. Make a table of squares, cubes, and fourth powers modulo 5. Solve the equations $x^2 = 1$, $x^3 = 1$, $x^4 = 1$ in this arithmetic.

2. Find $(x + y)^5$ modulo 5.

3. Divide $x^2 + 1$ by $x + 2$, modulo 5. Has $x^2 + 1 = 0$ any solutions in this arithmetic? What are they?

4. In the text we solved $x^2 + x = 2$, modulo 5. This equation may be written $x^2 + x + 3 = 0$. What are the factors of $x^2 + x + 3$?

5. Find by trial, by completing the square, or by any other method, the solutions of the following equations in the arithmetic modulo 5: (i) $x^2 + 2x + 2 = 0$, (ii) $x^2 + 3x + 1 = 0$, (iii) $x^2 + x + 4 = 0$, (iv) $x^2 + 4 = 0$. What are the factors of the quadratic expressions that occur in the equations above?

6. Divide $x^3 + 2x^2 + 3x + 4$ by $x - 2$ in the arithmetic modulo 5.

7. Does the remainder theorem hold in the arithmetic modulo 5?

8. Does the equation $(x - 3)^2 = 0$ have any solution other than $x = 3$ in the arithmetic modulo 4?

9. In the arithmetic modulo 6 calculate the values of $x^2 + 3x + 2$ for $x = 0, 1, 2, 3, 4, 5$. How many roots does the quadratic equation $x^2 + 3x + 2 = 0$ have in this arithmetic?

10. All the statements (*1*) through (*12*) are true in the arithmetic modulo 5. Which of them hold in (i) the arithmetic modulo 4, (ii) the arithmetic modulo 6?

11. Can it be proved that a quadratic equation has at most two roots (i) in an arithmetic where statements (*1*) through (*9*)

and (*11*) only are known to hold? (ii) in an arithmetic where statements (*7*) through (*12*) are known to hold?

12. In the arithmetic modulo 5 are there any quadratics $x^2 + px + q$ (i) that have no solutions when equated to zero? (ii) that cannot be split into factors of the form $(x + a)(x + b)$?

13. In the arithmetic modulo 5 the equation $x^3 = 2$ has the solution 3. Has it any other solutions? Divide $x^3 - 2$ by $x - 3$. Has the resulting quadratic any factors?

Chapter 2

Arithmetics and Polynomials

WE HAVE NOW met three kinds of arithmetic. Our ordinary arithmetic is the first kind. It deals with numbers 0, 1, 2, $\cdots$, that go on forever.

The arithmetic modulo 5 is the second kind. It contains only 0, 1, 2, 3, 4, but in spite of this it is remarkably like ordinary arithmetic. I can still ask you quite conventional questions in algebra—to multiply expressions, to do long division, to solve a quadratic, to factor a polynomial, to prove the remainder theorem.

The third type is shown by arithmetic modulo 4 or modulo 6. It diverges still further from ordinary arithmetic. A quadratic may have more than two roots; still more striking, division ceases to be possible. In modulo 6 arithmetic, $3 \div 2$ has no answer, while $4 \div 2$ has the answers 2 and 5. However, some similarities to ordinary arithmetic remain. We can still multiply without restriction. We can divide by 1 and 5, and this means that we can divide by $x - a$ or $5x - a$. The remainder theorem, that a polynomial $f(x)$ on division by $x - a$ leaves the remainder $f(a)$, still makes sense and is true.

It will be helpful in considering these arithmetics, and other structures that we shall meet, to tabulate their properties. On the left side of our table, we write our

Statements	Rational numbers	Natural numbers	Integers	Modulo 5	Modulo 6
(1) $a + b$ defined	+	+	+	+	+
(2) ab defined	+	+	+	+	+
(3) $a + b = b + a$	+	+	+	+	+
(4) $ab = ba$	+	+	+	+	+
(5) $a + (b + c) = (a + b) + c$	+	+	+	+	+
(6) $a(bc) = (ab)c$	+	+	+	+	+
(7) $a(b + c) = ab + ac$	+	+	+	+	+
(8) $b - a$ exists unique	+	0	+	+	+
(9) 0 exists	+	+	+	+	+
→ (10) b/a exists unique	+	0	0	+	0
(11) 1 exists	+	+	+	+	+
(12) $ab = 0$ only if $a = 0$ or $b = 0$	+	+	+	+	0

statements (*1*) through (*12*). Across the top of the table
we write the names of the structures we plan to "test."
If a structure satisfies the tests, or statements, we enter
a plus sign in the proper column. If a structure fails to
satisfy a test, or statement, we enter a zero. It is often
the property that is *lacking* that gives a peculiar flavor.

Across the top of our table we have the following structures listed: (i) The rational numbers; (ii) The natural
numbers 0, 1, 2, $\cdots$; (iii) The integers 0, ± 1, ± 2, $\cdots$;
(iv) The arithmetic modulo 5; (v) The arithmetic mod-
ulo 6.

In future, we shall define various types of structures by
saying which tests are passed. A table of this kind gives
a convenient way of recording definitions and of classify-
ing any particular structure.

We shall give one such definition straight away. Our
table shows two structures that make exactly the same
score—the rational numbers and the arithmetic modulo 5. Now we have had several examples to show that
you can work modulo 5 very much as you do in ordinary
arithmetic. We therefore introduce a name to express
this kind of similarity.

DEFINITION. *Any structure that passes all the tests* (*1*)
through (*12*) *is called a field.*

It is hard to hold all the twelve tests in mind at once,
and a rather looser explanation may be easier to remember. A field is a structure in which you can add, subtract,
multiply, and divide, and these operations behave very
much as they do in elementary arithmetic. Tests (*1*)
through (*12*) make precise what I mean by "behave
very much alike."

It may be well to collect together the twelve tests,
and to state them in a way that we can use generally.
Several of them were stated above in terms of the child
in the Pacific Island.

Every structure we consider contains elements. We are not concerned with what these elements are; they may be marks on paper, sounds of words, physical objects, parts of a calculating machine, thoughts in the mind. We also have operations $+$, $\times$ or $+$, $\cdot$. These operations need not have any connection with addition and multiplication in arithmetic, other than the purely formal resemblance required by the tests below. We think again of our calculating machine, with two spaces for elements a, b; one space for a sign $+$ or $\cdot$; and a space for the answer. We understand by $a + b$ or $a \cdot b$ what appears in the answer space—regardless of the internal mechanism of the calculating machine.

The following twelve statements will henceforth be referred to as the axioms for a field.

(1) *To any two elements a, b and the operation $+$, there corresponds a uniquely defined element c. We write $c = a + b$.*

(2) *To any two elements a, b and the operation $\cdot$, there corresponds a uniquely defined element d. We write $d = a \cdot b$.*

(3) $a + b = b + a$, *for all elements a, b.*

(4) $a \cdot b = b \cdot a$, *for all elements a, b.*

(5) $a + (b + c) = (a + b) + c$, *for all elements a, b, c.*

(6) $a \cdot (b \cdot c) = (a \cdot b) \cdot c$, *for all elements a, b, c.*

(7) $a \cdot (b + c) = (a \cdot b) + (a \cdot c)$, *for all elements a, b, c.*

(8) *For any elements a and b, we can find one and only one element x such that $a + x = b$. We call this element $b - a$.*

(9) *There is a unique element 0 such that $a + 0 = a$ for every element a.*

(10) *For any elements a and b, provided only that a is not 0, there is one and only one element x such that $ax = b$. We call this element b/a.*

(11) *There is a unique element 1 such that for every a, $a \cdot 1 =$*
    The element 1 is not the same as the element 0.

(12) $a \cdot b = 0$ *only if $a = 0$ or $b = 0$.*

(Students sometimes ask, "Ought we not include
an axiom that $a \cdot 0 = 0$ for all a?" This, however, ca
he proved from the axioms we already have. By axioms (9
and (11), $1 + 0 = 1$. Therefore, $a \cdot (1 + 0) = a \cdot 1$. By ax
iom (7), $a \cdot 1 + a \cdot 0 = a \cdot 1$. By axiom (11), $a + a \cdot 0 =$
This says that $x = a \cdot 0$ satisfies the equation $a + x =$
Axiom (8) shows that this equation has only one solu
tion. Axiom (9) states that this solution is $x = 0$. S
$a \cdot 0 = 0$. Note that axiom (12) is intended to be rea
in this sense: "If you know that ab is zero, you can deduc
that either a is zero or b is zero." The result we hav
just proved is the converse of this.)

In all of these axioms it should be understood that b
"element" we mean an element in the structure. Fc
instance, suppose we are applying the tests to the na
ural numbers 0, 1, 2, 3, $\cdots$. Someone might say, "Te
(10) is passed, because if you take any quotient lik
$3 \div 4$ it does exist; it is 3/4." But 3/4 is not an elemen
in the set 0, 1, 2, 3, $\cdots$. It is true that by *bringing in ne*
elements 1/2, 3/4, -1, -2, and so on, you can obtain
field, the field of rational numbers in which division an
subtraction are always possible. When we say that
structure is a field, we mean that it already contain
the answers to every subtraction and division question
A child that only knows the numbers 0, 1, 2, 3, $\cdots$, ca
only answer the questions "Take 4 from 3," "Divide
by 4" by saying "You can't take 4 from 3," "4 doesn'
go into 3." This indicates that the natural numbers d
not form a field; they fail tests (8) and (10).

I have not attempted to reduce the tests to the smalles
possible number, as might be done in a study of axiomat
ics. For instance, it is quite easy to show that a structur

that passes tests (*1*) through (*11*) also passes (*12*). Some of my tests could be cut down somewhat; part could be assumed and the remainder proved. My purpose at present is to explain what a field is, and to give a speedy way of recognizing one.

EXERCISES

Determine which of the following are fields, and show on the chart which tests each passes. (At this stage you may find it best to convince yourself that certain properties do or do not apⁿly, without necessarily being able to provide formal proof.)

1. The even numbers, 0, 2, 4, 6, $\cdots$.

2. The even numbers, including negative numbers, 0, ± 2, ± 4, $\cdots$.

3. The real numbers.

4. The complex numbers, $x + iy$, where x, y are real.

5. The complex numbers, $p + iq$, where p, q are rational.

6. The complex numbers, $m + in$, where m, n are integers.

7. All numbers of the form $p + q\sqrt{2}$, where p, q are rational.

8. All expressions $a + bx$, where a, b are real numbers.

9. All polynomials in x with real coefficients.

10. All functions $P(x)/Q(x)$, where $P(x)$ and $Q(x)$ are polynomials with real coefficients.

11. Arithmetic modulo 2.

12. Arithmetic modulo 3.

13. Arithmetic modulo 4.

Question for Investigation

If n is a positive whole number, what condition must n satisfy if the arithmetic modulo n is to be a field? It is fairly easy to find out experimentally what the condition is. It is also easy to show that the condition is necessary; that is, that arithmetic modulo n cannot be a field unless n has a certain property. It is harder to prove that this property is sufficient to ensure the arithmetic being a field.

A field is so much like our ordinary arithmetic that we can work with its elements just as if they were ordinary numbers; our usual habits lead us to correct results, and we feel quite at home.

But some structures, as we have seen, are provided with operations that we can label $+$ and $\cdot$, but yet fall short of being fields. One or more of statements (1) through (12) proves false.

There are still other structures in which we do not have two operations, but only one. For example, we might consider the structure in which every element was of the form "x dogs and y cats," x and y of course being positive whole numbers, or zero. It would be natural to have the operation $+$ defined to correspond to the word "and."

If a is 3 dogs and 4 cats,
      b is 5 dogs and 6 cats,
    $a + b$ is 8 dogs and 10 cats.

But there is no obvious way of defining the operation $\cdot$; we can hardly say that dog times dog is a square dog. We shall later meet less frivolous examples in which only one operation, either $+$ or $\cdot$ occurs.

These are, of course, simpler structures than arithmetic, and logically it would be reasonable to start with them and work up to arithmetic and other structures with two operations. However, it seemed wiser to start with the familiar subject of arithmetic, and only at

his stage to indicate that it occupies a fairly lofty posi-
ion in the family of all possible structures.

One might go beyond arithmetic to study structures
vith three operations, $+$, $\cdot$, and $*$ say. Whether any-
hing of mathematical interest or value would be found
n this way, I do not know.

Polynomials Over Any Field

The examples in chapter 1 suggested very strongly
hat most of the properties of polynomials in ordinary
lgebra were also true when we were working with the
rithmetic modulo 5. It should be possible to generalize
rom this, and to find properties true for any field F—
hat is to say, for any system obeying axioms (7) through
12).

When we write the quadratic $ax^2 + bx + c$, we may
ave in mind, for example,

  (i) a, b, c integers,
 (ii) a, b, c rational numbers,
(iii) a, b, c real numbers,
 (iv) a, b, c complex numbers,
  (v) a, b, c 0 or 1 in the arithmetic modulo 2,
 (vi) a, b, c 0, 1, 2, 3, or 4 in the arithmetic modulo 5.

In case (i) we say that $ax^2 + bx + c$ is a quadratic
polynomial *over the integers*. Thus $11x^2 - 4x + 3$ is a
polynomial over the integers.

In case (ii) we speak of a polynomial over the field of
ational numbers; for example, $\frac{1}{2}x^2 - \frac{3}{4}x + \frac{7}{8}$.

In case (iii) we have a polynomial over the field of
eal numbers; for example $x^2 + \pi x - e$.

In case (iv) we have a polynomial over the field of
omplex numbers; for example, $(1 + i)x^2 + (\frac{1}{2} - i)x + 3 + 4i)$.

In case (v) we have a quadratic over the arithmetic modulo 2; for example $1x^2 + 0x + 1$.

In case (vi) we have a quadratic over the arithmetic modulo 5; say, $2x^2 + 3x + 1$. This does not look any different from a quadratic over the integers. Perhaps if we write $(2x^2 + 3x + 1) \equiv 2(x + 1)(x + 3)$, the distinction will become apparent. You could, if you like, use a symbolism we had earlier, and write $IIx^2 + IIIx + I$ where the Roman numerals emphasize that we are dealing with numbers modulo 5.

The word "over" has always seemed to me a little queer in this connection. Perhaps it is used because the coefficients can range *over* the elements of the field F. Anyway, all that matters is its meaning. $ax^n + bx^{n-1} + \cdots + kx + m$ is a polynomial over the field F, if a, b, $\cdots$, k, m are all elements of F. The idea is a simple one.

The Scope of x

The step we have just taken corresponds to the beginning of school algebra. a, b, $\cdots$, k, m are numbers of the arithmetic (see examples (i) through (vi) of the previous subheading). The symbol x is something new. We have passed from 11, -4, 3 to $11x^2 - 4x + 3$.

The best pupils are not deceived by the apparent newness. They say, "You can test whether a statement about x is true by seeing whether it holds for any number." The worst pupils do not look at it this way. They have no idea what x means, but they manage to pick up certain rules for working with x.

Curiously enough, both points of view are significant for modern algebra. They lead to an important distinction. There are certain expressions (in certain fields F) that are equal when x is replaced by any number of the

field, but they are not equal in the sense of being the
same expression. The best pupils will say they are equal;
the worst pupils will say they are not.

An example will make this clear. Suppose our field F
consists of the numbers 0, 1 of arithmetic modulo 2. If
we ask a dull pupil "Is $x^2 + x$ equal to 0?" the pupil will
say "No." We ask, "Why?" The pupil answers, "Well,
they are different. $x^2 + x$ is $x^2 + x$, and 0 is 0. They are
two different things."

If we ask a bright pupil, who thinks of algebra as gen-
eralized arithmetic, "Is $x^2 + x$ equal to 0 in the arithmetic modulo 2?" this pupil will answer, "Let me see.
If x was 0, $x^2 + x$ would be 0. If x was 1, $x^2 + x$ would
be $1 + 1$, which is 0. 0 and 1 are the only numbers in
the field F. Yes; $x^2 + x$ is always the same number as 0."

Actually, we have to regard both answers as correct.
They are in effect answers to two different questions;
they correspond to two different interpretations of *equal*.
We shall need both of these ideas, and some agreed way
of expressing them.

If $f(x)$ and $g(x)$ are two algebraic expressions which,
when simplified in accordance with the rules of an
algebra, lead to one and the same polynomial $ax^n +
x^{n-1} + \cdots + kx + m$, we say that $f(x)$ and $g(x)$ are
formally equal.

If in $f(x)$ and $g(x)$, when we replace the symbol x by
any element of the field F, the resulting values are the
same, we say $f(x)$ equals $g(x)$ for every x in the field F.

Thus, for modulo 2 arithmetic, $x^2 + x$ and 0 are not
formally equal, but they are equal for every x in the field.

In ordinary algebra, it is not necessary to make this
distinction. There is a well-known theorem that if $f(x)$
and $g(x)$ are two polynomials equal for all rational numbers (or even for all integers), then $f(x)$ and $g(x)$ are
formally equal.

In a field with a finite number of elements, this distinction is bound to arise. For instance, arithmetic
modulo 3 contains only the numbers 0, 1, 2. Evidently
$x(x - 1)(x - 2)$ is zero for $x = 0$, for $x = 1$, and for
$x = 2$. So $x(x - 1)(x - 2) = 0$ for every x in the field.
But if you multiply this expression out, you get an answer
which is not $0x^3 + 0x^2 + 0x + 0$. So $x(x - 1)(x - 2)$ is
not formally equal to zero.

Question: Multiply out $x(x - 1)(x - 2)$ modulo 3.
Find and multiply out the corresponding expression for
the arithmetic modulo 5.

The fact just noted can be important. For instance,
the equation $x^2 = 2$ has no solution in the field F consisting of 0, 1, 2 modulo 3. We might want to bring in
a new sign, $\sqrt{2}$, and extend our arithmetic just as we do
with ordinary numbers. Now $x(x - 1)(x - 2)$ is *not* zero
for $x = \sqrt{2}$. If we are going to extend our number
system in this way, it is the dull child's answer and not
the bright one's that is helpful!

There are in fact three roles that x can play: (i) It may
stand for any element of the field F. (ii) It may stand for
certain elements outside the field F. (iii) It may not stand
for anything at all—it may be just a mark on a calculating machine.

Ordinary high school algebra is a sufficient example
of (i), where it is understood that any statement about
x holds for every number of arithmetic.

As an example of (ii) we might consider, say, $\frac{1}{2}x^2 +$
$\frac{3}{4}x - 5$. This is a polynomial over the rationals. But we
can consider the result of putting $x = \sqrt{2}$ or $x = \pi$ in
this expression. Neither number is rational.

A more striking example can be found from calculus.
(This is simply an example. Any student unfamiliar
with calculus can omit it, as it is not needed for later

(evelopments.) Let $f(t)$ stand for any function of t that s capable of being differentiated as often as we wish. Let D stand for the operation d/dt so that

$$Df(t) = f'(t)$$
$$D^2f(t) = f''(t)$$
$$D^3f(t) = f'''(t) \quad \text{and so on.}$$

By an expression such as $(D^2 + 2D + 3)f(t)$, we shall understand $f''(t) + 2f'(t) + 3f(t)$. (This example is intended to convey what we understand by *addition* of the operations D^2, $2D$, and 3.)

Multiplication of operations means that the operations are to be applied successively. Thus, if I want to apply $(D + 2) \cdot (D + 3)$ to $f(t)$, I begin by finding $(D + 3)f(t)$. Let this be $u(t)$. I then apply the operation $(D + 2)$ to $u(t)$, and get $(D + 2)u(t)$, that is, $u'(t) + 2u(t)$, where $u(t) = (D + 3)f(t) = f'(t) + 3f(t)$. If I substitute this value of $u(t)$ in $u'(t) + 2u(t)$ I get

$$f''(t) + 3f'(t) + 2f'(t) + 6f(t) = f''(t) + 5f'(t) + 6f(t).$$

To summarize what we have done: Applying the operation $D + 3$ to $f(t)$ gives $f'(t) + 3f(t)$. Applying the operation $D + 2$ to the result above gives $f''(t) + 5f'(t) + 6f(t)$. This last expression is what we understand by $(D + 2) \cdot (D + 3)$ acting on $f(t)$.

But the result above could be written $(D^2 + 5D + 6)f(t)$. That is: the operation $(D + 2) \cdot (D + 3)$ applied to any function has the same effect as $D^2 + 5D + 6$ applied to the same function. We naturally call these two operations *equal*. In symbols

$$(D + 2) \cdot (D + 3) = D^2 + 5D + 6.$$

But this result has a familiar look. It is exactly what we should get if we forgot all about D standing for d/dt and simply applied the rules of elementary algebra.

Thus, in certain circumstances, we are entitled to

substitute in $x^2 + 5x + 6$ the value $x = d/dt$, which i
not a number at all. This fact is made use of in teaching
engineering students how to solve certain types of differ
ential equations.

Finally, we may—as we did toward the end of the
last example—say "let us forget all about the meaning
of x, and simply remember than x may be manipulated
according to certain rules." This is the fully abstrac
approach. It corresponds to possibility (iii) above.

The kind of theorem that can be obtained by the ab
stract approach is shown by the following importan
result. If you have a calculating machine with certai
signs marked on it (the numbers or elements of F) an
also two operations, $+$ and $\cdot$, for which the twelv
field axioms hold, then you can build a calculating
machine that will have all those signs and also the signs
x, x^2, x^3, $\cdots$. On this enlarged machine, addition an
multiplication will still be possible; the commutative
associative, and distributive laws will still hold.

In other words, if you have any field F, and you in
troduce a new symbol x without inquiring at all into th
meaning of x, and you perform calculations with poly
nomials in x (the coefficients being elements of F) b
means of the ordinary rules of algebra, then you will no
arrive at any contradiction. I have not yet proved thi
to be so. I have only indicated the kind of theorem tha
can be arrived at by the purely abstract approach.

What do we actually use when we are making calcu
lations with polynomials? Suppose, for instance, we ar
multiplying $(ax^2 + bx + c)(dx + e)$. If we proceed i
great detail, we write

$$(ax^2 + bx + c)(dx + e)$$
$$= (ax^2 + bx + c)dx + (ax^2 + bx + c)e$$
$$= ax^2 \cdot dx + bx \cdot dx + c \cdot dx + ax^2 \cdot e + bx \cdot e + ce$$

So far we have used the associative law for addition, and distributive laws. These are not covered by axioms (1) through (12), which refer only to elements of the field F. But we have here also the symbol x, to which no meaning attaches, and which, accordingly, we cannot regard as being an element of F.

To deal with a term like $ax^2 \cdot dx$ we have to use associative and commutative laws for multiplication, and we write

$$(ax^2)(dx) = a(x^2 \cdot dx)$$
$$= a(dx \cdot x^2)$$
$$= a(d \cdot xx^2)$$
$$= a(d \cdot x^3)$$
$$= (ad)x^3.$$

ad, of course, is an element of F.

It would therefore be sufficient if we said, "Given a field F and a symbol x, we assume that the associative, commutative, and distributive laws hold not only for the elements of F, but also when the elements are combined in any way with x and its powers."

This would certainly serve as a very useful axiom and would allow us to establish the usual procedures for calculations with polynomials. But by what right could we bring in such an additional axiom? How do we know that such an element x can be joined on to any field? Might not a contradiction be produced by bringing in this extra axiom? Or at any rate, some extra information about F? There might be things we could prove about the elements of F themselves (that is, with no mention of x) with the help of this extra axiom, that we could not prove without it.

Now in fact, with any field F, you can study polynomials over that field. In so doing you do not place any restrictions on F nor do you bring in any contradictions.

This is going to be something of a foundation stone for our future work, and we do not want to have any doubts about it.

We want to show that if we have a calculating machine for an arithmetic 0, 1, $\cdots$, we can always produce a calculating machine for an algebra 0, 1, $\cdots$, x. How are we going to get this new symbol x joined on to the existing symbols 0, 1, $\cdots$?

How could we show on a calculating machine the quadratic $2x^2 + 3x + 4$? A quadratic is specified by three numbers—the coefficient of x^2, the coefficient of x, and the constant term. A machine for displaying quadratics might have the following form.

Constant term	Coefficient of x	Coefficient of x^2
④	③	②

Suppose the machine had to add quadratics. It might appear as follows.

First quadratic	④	③	②
Second quadratic	⑤	⑦	①
Sum	⑨	⑩	③

It is very noticeable here that we have *no reference at all* to x. On the outside of the calculating machine there might be painted (for the benefit of inexperienced operators) the words "Constant term; coefficient of x; coefficient of x^2." But if the paint wore off, the machine would still work just as well.

From the point of view of the designer of calculating machines, then, the quadratic $a + bx + cx^2$ is simply defined by the three numbers (a, b, c). The quadratic $\alpha + \beta x + \gamma x^2$ is something defined by the three numbers (α, β, γ). The sum of the quadratics is something defined by the three terms $(a + \alpha, b + \beta, c + \gamma)$.

What about the product?

$$(a + bx + cx^2)(\alpha + \beta x + \gamma x^2) = a\alpha + (a\beta + b\alpha)x$$
$$+ (a\gamma + b\beta + c\alpha)x^2 + (b\gamma + c\beta)x^3 + c\gamma x^4.$$

The product is thus something defined by the sequence of numbers

$$a\alpha, \ a\beta + b\alpha, \ a\gamma + b\beta + c\alpha, \ b\gamma + c\beta, \ c\gamma.$$

Our example above, with the calculating machine showing two quadratics, could thus be extended as follows.

First quadratic	④	③	②		
Second quadratic	⑤	⑦	①		
Sum	⑨	⑩	③		
Product	⑳	㊸	㉟	⑰	②

The machine so far seems designed only for multiplying quadratics. We should like it to deal with polynomials of any reasonable degree. A machine that would multiply polynomials, provided the answer was not above the seventh degree, would have the following appearance when set for the two quadratics above.

First polynomial	④	③	②	⓪	⓪	⓪	⓪	⓪
Second polynomial	⑤	⑦	①	⓪	⓪	⓪	⓪	⓪
Sum	⑨	⑩	③	⓪	⓪	⓪	⓪	⓪
Product	⑳	㊸	㉟	⑰	②	⓪	⓪	⓪

You will notice how completely x has disappeared from the scheme. We think, of course, of the columns as corresponding to $1, x, x^2, x^3, \cdots$, but this thought is, so far, not embodied in the machine.

I do not know if you feel worried by a sense of the machine being incomplete. It would be unable to give the correct answer for the product of two polynomials of the fifth degree, and it would not even be able to state the problem of multiplying two polynomials of the ninth degree. Only a machine with an infinite number of columns would be free from this kind of limitation, and one is naturally hesitant to talk about such a thing.

We could get round this difficulty with a machine like an electronic calculator, where instructions go in on tape and a printed answer comes out.

The problem would go in something like this.

> First polynomial: 4, 3, 2, finish.
> Second polynomial: 5, 7, 1, finish.
> Operation: multiply.

The answer would come out as

> Answer: 20, 43, 35, 17, 2, finish.

If the first polynomial had $(m + 1)$ numbers in it, and the second one $(n + 1)$ numbers, the answer would contain $(m + n + 1)$ numbers.

Infinity does not trouble the construction of this machine, and I think we could have easy consciences in talking about it. And yet, in a way, an infinity of zeros is implied, even in a finite expression like $4 + 3x + 2x^2$. If you ask me "What is the coefficient of x^3 here?" I answer "Zero." If you ask me, "What is the coefficient of x^4" I answer "Zero." The same for $x^{1,000,000}$ and $x^{1,000,000,000}$.

Thus, if I write "4, 3, 2, 0, 0, 0, 0, $\cdots$, on forever," I am not doing much different from making the finite statement, "4, 3, 2, finish."

Accordingly, I shall feel free to talk about 4, 3, 2, 0, 0, 0, $\cdots$, an infinite sequence, in the belief that this is not a vicious use of infinity.

The operation that the machine does when it multiplies two polynomials can be put in a more explicit form.

If you look at the number $a\gamma + b\beta + c\alpha$ that occurs in the product of

$$
\begin{array}{ccc}
a & b & c \\
\alpha & \beta & \gamma
\end{array}
$$

you may observe a pattern in it. This pattern can be felt in the muscles, if you put a forefinger on the Latin letter and a thumb on the Greek letter of the rows above, for each term, as you read $a\gamma + b\beta + c\alpha$. Your finger will move forward through a, b, c as your thumb moves backward through α, β, γ.

A pattern of this kind appears most clearly if suffix notation is used. The product of

$$
\begin{array}{ccc}
p_0 & p_1 & p_2 \\
q_0 & q_1 & q_2
\end{array}
$$

contains the following numbers

$$
\begin{aligned}
& p_0 q_0, \\
& p_0 q_1 + p_1 q_0, \\
& p_0 q_2 + p_1 q_1 + p_2 q_2, \\
& p_1 q_2 + p_2 q_1, \\
& p_2 q_2.
\end{aligned}
$$

Question: What do you notice about the suffixes here? If we multiply

$$
\begin{array}{ccccc}
p_0 & p_1 & p_2 & \cdots & p_m
\end{array}
$$

by

$$
\begin{array}{ccccc}
q_0 & q_1 & q_2 & \cdots & \cdots & q_n,
\end{array}
$$

how can the resulting numbers be expressed most compactly?

Your solution to this question will, I am sure, be equivalent to the following.

Let the product be $k_0, k_1, \cdots, k_{m+n}$. Then

$$
\begin{aligned}
k_0 &= p_0 q_0, \\
k_1 &= p_0 q_1 + p_1 q_0, \\
k_2 &= p_0 q_2 + p_1 q_1 + p_2 q_0, \quad \text{and so on.}
\end{aligned}
$$

In k_0 the suffixes add up to zero, in k_1 they add up to 1, in k_2 to 2, and so on. In k_r we expect the indices to add up to r. If p_s occurs in k_r, its partner must be q_{r-s}. We are thus led to write

$$k_r = \sum_{s=0}^{s=r} p_s q_{r-s}.$$

It is understood, of course, that for $s > m$, $p_s = 0$ and for $t > n$, $q_t = 0$. This corresponds to our remark that in the first row p_m is followed by endless zeros, and similarly for q_n in the second row.

We have now arrived at a fair specification of a polynomial machine. A polynomial machine contains columns into which we can enter numbers of the field F. By "a polynomial of degree m" we understand that the machine is set so as to show "$p_0, p_1, p_2, \cdots, p_m$ finish" or, equivalently, "$p_0, p_1, p_2, \cdots, p_m, 0, 0, 0, \cdots,$" the zeros continuing forever. The input to the machine contains spaces for *two polynomials*, the first and second polynomials, say $(p_0, p_1, p_2, \cdots)$ and $(q_0, q_1, q_2, \cdots)$. The output of the machine shows two polynomials, namely the sum and product of the input polynomials. The sum is the polynomial $(j_0, j_1, j_2, \cdots)$, where $j_r = p_r + q_r$. The product is the polynomial $(k_0, k_1, k_2, \cdots)$, where

$$k_r = \sum_{s=0}^{s=r} p_s q_{r-s}.$$

The sum and product are defined for this new machine. We cannot immediately identify sum on the new machine with $+$ on the old, nor product on the new with $\cdot$ on the old. No doubt there is some relationship, but until we have established what it is, we had better use new signs for the new machine. I will use S for sum, P for product.

The old machine is a calculating machine for the

arithmetic of the field F. It adds and multiplies individual numbers.

The new machine deals with *sequences* such as $(4, 3, 2, 0, 0, 0, \cdots)$ and $(5, 7, 1, 0, 0, 0, \cdots)$. It gives results such as

$$(4, 3, 2, 0, 0, 0, \cdots) \text{ S } (5, 7, 1, 0, 0, 0, \cdots)$$
$$= (9, 10, 3, 0, 0, 0, \cdots)$$

and

$$(4, 3, 2, 0, 0, 0, \cdots) \text{ P } (5, 7, 1, 0, 0, 0, \cdots)$$
$$= (20, 43, 35, 17, 2, 0, 0, 0, \cdots).$$

We have noted above the rules by which the answers to ( ) S ( ) and ( ) P ( ) are obtained.

It is important to note that nothing is stated about the new machine except that it carries out these rules correctly. Nothing else whatever is assumed about the operations S and P. We know that the operations S and P can be carried out, because they depend simply on the operations of arithmetic in the field F. The old machine does arithmetic; the new machine will contain one or more replicas of the old machine, for doing the necessary arithmetic.

The two machines, the arithmetic machine (the old machine) and the polynomial machine (the new machine), are now set up. Their nature is determined. We cannot introduce any more assumptions. We can only observe the machines and see what they do. We have no more control over events. The machines must speak for themselves.

We can however introduce certain abbreviations. It will be convenient to have a short name for the sequence $(1, 0, 0, 0, \cdots)$. We shall call it **1**. **1** is not the number 1. It is not a number at all; it is a sequence. In the same way **4** is a convenient abbreviation for the sequence $(4, 0, 0, 0, \cdots)$.

The sequence $(0, 1, 0, 0, 0, \cdots)$ will also receive a name. If you think of how we originally arrived at these sequences, you will see what part this sequence is destined to play. It is the sequence we should use to represent the algebraic expression x. At last x is coming into the picture.

We accordingly define x as standing for the sequence $(0, 1, 0, 0, 0, \cdots)$.

In case you think anything mysterious is involved in saying that 1 is a name for $(1, 0, 0, 0, \cdots)$ and x is a name for $(0, 1, 0, 0, 0, \cdots)$, it may help you to see how simply these abbreviations can be embodied in the machine. All it means is that the operator has keys on which are written 1, 4, x, etc. If the operator presses 1, automatically the sequence $(1, 0, 0, 0, \cdots)$ appears. If the operator presses 4, then $(4, 0, 0, 0, \cdots)$ appears. If the operator presses the key marked x, then $(0, 1, 0, 0, 0, \cdots)$ will appear.

Suppose, for instance, that in setting up the first polynomial the operator simply presses the key marked x, and does the same for the second polynomial. The machine will carry out the operations S and P and we shall see the following.

First polynomial, x, $(0, 1, 0, 0, 0, \cdots)$
Second polynomial, x, $(0, 1, 0, 0, 0, \cdots)$
Sum $(0, 2, 0, 0, 0, \cdots)$
Product $(0, 0, 1, 0, 0, \cdots)$

You should check for yourself that the rules, by which the machine works, do lead to the results shown above.

Thus $(0, 0, 1, 0, 0, \cdots)$ has turned up as the result of multiplying x and x. It seems natural to provide a key marked x^2 that will automatically set up $(0, 0, 1, 0, 0, \cdots)$. We shall then be able to note the result, which the machine gives us as

$(0, 1, 0, 0, 0, \cdots)$ P $(0, 1, 0, 0, 0, \cdots)$
$$= (0, 0, 1, 0, 0, 0, \cdots),$$

in the shorter form,

$$x \text{ P } x = x^2.$$

Note that x^2 is a single sign. It is something marked on a particular key. When you press this key, you set $(0, 0, 1, 0, 0, 0, \cdots)$. I am not asserting that x^2 is the square of x or anything like that. You must remember that this is supposed to be the beginning of algebra. We have to pretend that you have never seen x^2 before; you know nothing of the implications of x^2 except what you can find out by operating the machine.

Now we feel tempted to rush ahead and say, "I see how things are working out. $(4, 3, 2, 0, 0, 0, \cdots)$ is going to get the label $4 + 3x + 2x^2$, or in the new notation $4 \text{ S } 3 \text{ P } x \text{ S } 2 \text{ P } x^2$." Now that is true enough in the long run, but we have to be careful not to be carried away by the familiar notation and make unjustified assumptions. $4 + 3x + 2x^2$ has no meaning in a formal system until the associative law for addition has been established; for otherwise $4 + (3x + 2x^2)$ and $(4 + 3x) + 2x^2$ might have different values, and we do not know which is intended. Also we think of $4 + (3x + 2x^2)$ and $(3x + 2x^2) + 4$ and $4 + (2x^2 + 3x)$ and $(2x^2 + 3x) + 4$ as all meaning the same thing. But this is not so, unless the commutative law has been established. Even the use of $2x^2$ normally implies that $(2x)x = 2(xx)$, that is, the associative law for multiplication. Different forms of bracketing give different results in a nonassociative system. $x(x(xx))$, $((xx)x)x$, and $(xx)(xx)$ may have quite different values. You can see this by considering, in ordinary algebra, the symbol

$$x^{x^{x^{x}}}.$$

"To the," as used in "a to the b," is a nonassociative operation. Without some convention or bracketing, $x^{x^{x^x}}$ could have several meanings.

(i) We might begin at the bottom and work up. Our calculation proceeds thus: $(x^x)^x = x^{(x^2)}$, and $\left(x^{x^2}\right)^x = x^{(x^3)}$.

(ii) We might bracket thus $(x^x)^{(x^x)}$. This equals $x^{x}(x^x) = x^{(x^x+1)}$.

(iii) Finally we might work from the top down. This is the meaning normally attached to $x^{x^{x^x}}$ since both (i) and (ii) lead to answers that could be written more simply.

Working from the top down, for example, with $2^{2^{2^2}}$ would give $2^2 = 4$, $2^{(2^2)} = 2^4 = 16$, and finally $2^{2^{2^2}} = 2^{16}$.

Thus bracketing is needed to give a definite meaning to

$$\text{"}x \text{ to the } x \text{ to the } x \text{ to the } x,\text{"}$$

and we must show good reason for it if we are going to use

$$\text{"}x \text{ times } x \text{ times } x \text{ times } x\text{"}$$

without any brackets.

We must in fact establish the five basic laws of algebra, which are usually written

    (I) $u + v = v + u$
   (II) $u \cdot v = v \cdot u$
 (III) $u + (v + w) = (u + v) + w$
 (IV) $u \cdot (vw) = (uv)w$
  (V) $u(v + w) = (uv) + (uw)$.

We have to establish these laws for polynomials, (sequences) u, v, w. We have agreed to use $+$ and $\cdot$ for operations on the old calculating machine (the arithmetic of the field F). On the new calculating machine (for polynomials over F), we have the operations S and P, and we must write the laws corresponding to (I) through (V) with these symbols thus

(I$'$) $u \text{ S } v = v \text{ S } u$
(II$'$) $u \text{ P } v = v \text{ P } u$
(III$'$) $u \text{ S } (v \text{ S } w) = (u \text{ S } v) \text{ S } w$
(IV$'$) $u \text{ P } (v \text{ P } w) = (u \text{ P } v) \text{ P } w$
(V$'$) $u \text{ P } (v \text{ S } w) = (u \text{ P } v) \text{ S } (u \text{ P } w).$

At least, we must do this if we want to be consistent. But the laws in the form first given, with $+$ and $\cdot$, look much more familiar and can be read at a glance. We can be forgiven if we sneak a look at them, to remind us of the part that laws (I$'$) through (V$'$) play.

We are of course forced to use different signs for addition and multiplication on the new machine; otherwise we should find ourselves assuming things in algebra that in fact we had only proved for arithmetic. Later, of course, when everything has been shown to work properly, we shall abandon P and S and replace them by $\cdot$ and $+$ for future use.

Now we are not in much doubt that laws (I$'$) through (V$'$) will work for polynomials, because, if you look back, you will see that we defined the operations S and P so that they gave a formal statement of what we do anyway in school algebra.

There is, however, one point to watch. While, in illustrations, I have been using the numbers of ordinary arithmetic—for example, 4, 3, 2, 0, 0,—the whole object of our present work is to show that we can build an algebra on *any* arithmetic. By an arithmetic here I mean a field F, a set of symbols obeying axioms (*1*) through (*12*). Now it might be that, in formulating these axioms, we have overlooked some important property. To make sure that this is not so, we have to prove that our algebra works properly, without appealing to anything except axioms (*1*) through (*12*). If we can carry this proof through, then we know that axioms (*1*) through (*12*) not only express interesting properties of a number system, but that they contain all the conditions an arithmetic must satisfy if an algebra of polynomials is to be based on it.

It is for this reason that some rather cautious formal work is now in order. We cannot say, "It's a waste of time to prove such results in detail. Anyone can see that the results are true, and only drudgery is needed to carry the checking through." The value of this formal work is not that it makes us more sure of the correctness of ordinary algebra but that it opens a whole new world to us. It assures us that if we have a system of elements, an arithmetic, we have only to verify that it satisfies the twelve axioms of a field, and then we shall be able to make algebraic calculations, on the basis of this arithmetic, *without learning any new habits.*

We now proceed to prove laws (I′) through (V′), for polynomials over any field F. (See the comments on page 3 of the introduction before reading farther.)

THEOREM (I′). *If u and v are polynomials over F, then* $u \, S \, v = v \, S \, u.$

Proof. Let u be the sequence $(a_0, a_1, a_2, \cdots)$ and v the sequence $(b_0, b_1, b_2, \cdots)$. It is understood here that a_i is an element of F, and that for $i > m$, $a_i = 0$. In the same way, b_i is an element of F, and if $i > n$, $b_i = 0$.

Let $u \, S \, v$ be $(e_0, e_1, e_2, \cdots)$ and $v \, S \, u$ be $(d_0, d_1, d_2, \cdots)$.

The definition of sum was given earlier. To find $u \, S \, v$, we take $p_r = a_r$, $q_r = b_r$ in this definition. We find $e_r = a_r + b_r$ for all r. To find $v \, S \, u$, we put $p_r = b_r$, $q_r = a_r$ in this definition.

We find $d_r = b_r + a_r$ for all r. But a_r and b_r are elements of F. By axiom (3), $a_r + b_r = b_r + a_r$.

$\therefore\ e_r = d_r$ for all r.

Therefore the sequences $(e_0, e_1, e_2, \cdots)$ and $(d_0, d_1, d_2, \cdots)$ are identical. $u\ \text{S}\ v = v\ \text{S}\ u$.   Q.E.D.

Although we have not mentioned it in this proof, axiom (1) is really involved here. Axiom (1) states that $a + b$ is defined for all elements a, b of F. Without this axiom, the definition of S would be meaningless.

In the same way, the definition of the operation P uses equations such as $k_2 = p_0 q_2 + p_1 q_1 + p_2 q_0$. This equation has a meaning only in virtue of: axiom (2), which allows us to speak of the products $p_0 q_2$, $p_1 q_1$, $p_2 q_0$; axiom (1), which allows us to add these; and axiom (5), which allows us to omit brackets in the addition.

THEOREM (II'). *If u and v are polynomials over F, then* $u\ \text{P}\ v = v\ \text{P}\ u$.

Proof: Let $u\ \text{P}\ v$ be $(f_0, f_1, f_2, \cdots)$ and $v\ \text{P}\ u$ be $(g_0, g_1, g_2, \cdots)$. We use the same symbols, $(a_0, a_1, a_2, \cdots)$ for u and $(b_0, b_1, b_2, \cdots)$ for v that were used in proving the preceding theorem.

In the definition of a product, let $p_i = a_i$ and $q_i = b_i$ for all i. Hence, writing the summation in full, we have

$$f_r = a_0 b_r + a_1 b_{r-1} + a_2 b_{r-2} + \cdots + a_r b_0.$$

Similarly, on putting $p_i = b_i$ and $q_i = a_i$, we obtain

$$g_r = b_0 a_r + b_1 a_{r-1} + b_2 a_{r-2} + \cdots + b_r a_0.$$

By axiom (3), $b_0 a_r + b_1 a_{r-1} = b_1 a_{r-1} + b_0 a_r$. Using this axiom repeatedly, we can get $b_0 a_r$ as the last term in the expression for g_r instead of the first. We can similarly work the term $b_1 a_{r-1}$ into the last place but one, by use of the same axiom. We can continue to rearrange the terms of g_r until the order has been completely reversed. Hence by repeated use of axiom (3), with axiom (5) in the background to justify the omission of brackets, we find

$$g_r = b_r a_0 + b_{r-1} a_1 + \cdots + b_1 a_{r-1} + b_0 a_r.$$

In each product, now use axiom (4).

$$\therefore g_r = a_0 b_r + a_1 b_{r-1} + \cdots + a_{r-1} b_1 + a_r b_0 = f_r.$$

Hence $u \, P \, v = v \, P \, u$.   Q.E.D.

THEOREM (III'). $u \, S \, (v \, S \, w) = (u \, S \, v) \, S \, w.$

Proof. Let u be $(a_0, a_1, a_2, \cdots)$, v be $(b_0, b_1, b_2, \cdots)$, and w be $(c_0, c_1, c_2, \cdots)$.

$u \, S \, (v \, S \, w)$ implies that we first combine v and w, and the result of this is combined with u. $v \, S \, w$ is $(b_0 + c_0, b_1 + c_1, b_2 + c_2, \cdots)$. Hence $u \, S \, (v \, S \, w)$ is

$$(a_0 + [b_0 + c_0], a_1 + [b_1 + c_1], a_2 + [b_2 + c_2], \cdots).$$

We now calculate the quantity on the right-hand side of the equation.

$u \, S \, v$ is

$$(a_0 + b_0, a_1 + b_1, a_2 + b_2, \cdots).$$

$(u \, S \, v) \, S \, w$ is

$$([a_0 + b_0] + c_0, [a_1 + b_1] + c_1, [a_2 + b_2] + c_2, \cdots).$$

By axiom (5), $a_i + (b_i + c_i) = (a_i + b_i) + c_i$ for all i, and hence the sequences are identical.

$$\therefore u \, S \, (v \, S \, w) = (u \, S \, v) \, S \, w \qquad \text{Q.E.D.}$$

THEOREM (IV'). $u \, P \, (v \, P \, w) = (u \, P \, v) \, P \, w.$

Proof. We keep the symbols for u, v, w that were used in proving the preceding theorem.

$v \, P \, w$ is the sequence

$$(b_0 c_0, \; b_0 c_1 + b_1 c_0, \; b_0 c_2 + b_1 c_1 + b_2 c_0,$$
$$b_0 c_3 + b_1 c_2 + b_2 c_1 + b_3 c_0, \; \cdots).$$

$u \, P \, (v \, P \, w)$ will thus be the sequence $(h_0, h_1, h_2, h_3, \cdots)$, where

$$h_0 = a_0(b_0c_0),$$
$$h_1 = a_0(b_0c_1 + b_1c_0) + a_1(b_0c_0),$$
$$h_2 = a_0(b_0c_2 + b_1c_1 + b_2c_0) + a_1(b_0c_1 + b_1c_0) + a_2(b_0c_0),$$

and so on.

We arrive at $(u \text{ P } v) \text{ P } w$ by seeing that $(u \text{ P } v)$ is

$$(a_0b_0, \; a_0b_1 + a_1b_0, \; a_0b_2 + a_1b_1 + a_2b_0,$$
$$a_0b_3 + a_1b_2 + a_2b_1 + a_3b_0, \cdots).$$

So $(u \text{ P } v) \text{ P } w$ is $(k_0, k_1, k_2, \cdots)$, where

$$k_0 = (a_0b_0)c_0,$$
$$k_1 = (a_0b_0)c_1 + (a_0b_1 + a_1b_0)c_0,$$
$$k_2 = (a_0b_0)c_2 + (a_0b_1 + a_1b_0)c_1 + (a_0b_2 + a_1b_1 + a_2b_0)c_0,$$

and so on.

Now, in these particular cases, it is easy to multiply out the expressions for h_0, h_1, h_2, and k_0, k_1, k_2 and see that equal expressions result. h_0, h_1, h_2 can be multiplied out directly by appealing to axiom (7). We cannot apply axiom (7) directly to finding k_1 and k_2, since axiom (7) deals with $a(b + c)$. It says nothing about $(b + c)a$! But this does not delay us for long.

For $\quad (b + c)a = a(b + c)$,   by axiom (4)
$$= ab + ac, \quad \text{by axiom (7)}$$
$$= ba + ca, \quad \text{by axiom (4)}.$$

It is easy to deduce that

$$(b + c + d)a = ba + ca + da,$$

since $b + c + d = (b + c) + d$. The result above has to be used twice. Similarly we prove

$$(b + c + d + \cdots + j)a = ba + ca + da + \cdots + ja.$$

We can thus verify $h_0 = k_0$, $h_1 = k_1$, $h_2 = k_2$. This makes it plausible that $h_r = k_r$ for all r, but of course it does not *prove* that it is so. It would require an eternity to work out all the individual results. To finish our proof we must find some way of *describing* h_r and k_r, from which it will become evident that $h_r = k_r$ for all r.

If you look at h_2 you will notice that the suffixes of a, b, c add up to 2 in each term. In fact, h_2 contains all the terms $a_s b_t c_w$ for which $s + t + w = 2$, and each combination s, t, w occurs once only. The same is true of k_2. (There is nothing surprising about this result. It provides, in fact, a method of elementary algebra for multiplying polynomials.)

In general, we can show that both h_r and k_r are equal to $\Sigma a_s b_t c_w$ over all s, t, w for which $s + t + w = r$.

The only difficulty in giving a proof of this result is a difficulty very characteristic of logical analysis. There is a stage when the facts to be proved are so evident that you do not know just how much commentary is called for. One faces this kind of difficulty, for instance, if asked to prove $4 + 5 = 9$. If someone questions $4 + 5$ being 9, we wonder what he accepts that will serve as a basis for the proof.

The same kind of difficulty arises here. It is pretty evident that h_r does contain all the terms $a_s b_t c_w$ such that $s + t + w = r$. The difficulty is to see just what one must say to justify it. The simplest course is to write, "Obviously it is so."

I think what we have to establish is the following.

(i) If $s + t + w = r$, $a_s b_t c_w$ occurs in the expression for h_r.

(ii) It occurs once only. (Note that $a_1 b_2 c_3$ is not the same as $a_2 b_3 c_1$. Both of these will occur in h_6.)

(iii) No term occurs in h_r other than the type mentioned in (i) above.

The same of course must be proved for k_r.

Conditions (i), (ii), and (iii) are easily verified. Let v P w be $(j_0, j_1, j_2, \cdots)$. Then, by the definition of P,

$$j_i = b_0 c_i + b_1 c_{i-1} + b_2 c_{i-2} + \cdots + b_i c_0.$$

Since u P $(v$ P $w)$ is $(h_0, h_1, h_2, \cdots)$, we have

$$h_r = a_0 j_r + a_1 j_{r-1} + a_2 j_{r-2} + \cdots + a_r j_0.$$

We want to prove, for (i), that if $s + t + w = r$, then $a_s b_t c_w$ occurs in h_r.

Now h_r contains $a_s j_{r-s}$. As $r - s = t + w$, $a_s j_{r-s} = a_s j_{t+w}$. j_{t+w} contains $b_t c_w$. Hence the term $a_s b_t c_w$ does appear in h_r. (It cannot cancel, since no negative terms are involved.)

Next, for (ii), we must show that $a_s b_t c_w$ occurs once only. In h_r, a_s occurs only in $a_s j_{r-s}$.* And j_{r-s}, that is, j_{t+w}, contains only one term involving b_t, namely $b_t c_w$. Thus $a_s b_t c_w$ cannot occur more than once.

Finally, we prove (iii). h_r is the sum of expressions $a_s j_{r-s}$, and j_{r-s} is the sum of terms $b_t c_{r-s-t}$. Hence every term appearing in h_r is of the form $a_s b_t c_{r-s-t}$, that is to say, of the form $a_s b_t c_w$ where $r = s + t + w$.

We have now completed the proof that h_r is as stated. A similar argument can be carried through for k_r. Hence $h_r = k_r$ for all r, and Theorem (IV') is proved. Q.E.D.

THEOREM (v'). $u \, \text{P} \, (v \, \text{S} \, w) = (u \, \text{P} \, v) \, \text{S} \, (u \, \text{P} \, w)$.

Fortunately the proof of this theorem is much shorter. It consists simply of a direct verification.

$v \, \text{S} \, w$ is the sequence $(b_0 + c_0, \ b_1 + c_1, \ b_2 + c_2, \ \cdots)$. $u \, \text{P} \, (v \, \text{S} \, w)$ is then $(y_0, y_1, y_2, \cdots)$, where

$$y_r = a_0(b_r + c_r) + a_1(b_{r-1} + c_{r-1}) + \cdots + a_r(b_0 + c_0).$$

On the right-hand side, $u \, \text{P} \, v$ is $(f_0, f_1, f_2, \cdots)$, where

$$f_r = a_0 b_r + a_1 b_{r-1} + \cdots + a_r b_0.$$

$u \, \text{P} \, w$ is $(z_0, z_1, z_2, \cdots)$, where

$$z_r = a_0 c_r + a_1 c_{r-1} + \cdots + a_r c_0.$$

---

* The trouble with this kind of analysis is that you start asking yourself, "How do I know that a_s only occurs once? Ought I to prove that it does?" Every analysis must stop somewhere. We may as well be firm. We have no doubt that the statement just made is true. We stop here. Future generations can get their Ph.D.'s in mathematical philosophy by analyzing this statement if they want to.

The theorem requires us to show that $y_r = f_r + z_r$ for all r. But

$$
\begin{aligned}
f_r + z_r &= (a_0b_r + a_1b_{r-1} + \cdots + a_rb_0) \\
&\quad + (a_0c_r + a_1c_{r-1} + \cdots + a_rc_0) \\
&= (a_0b_r + a_0c_r) + (a_1b_{r-1} + a_1c_{r-1}) + \cdots \\
&\quad + (a_rb_0 + a_rc_0) \text{ by repeated use of axioms} \\
&\qquad (3) \text{ and } (5), \\
&= a_0(b_r + c_r) + a_1(b_{r-1} + c_{r-1}) + \cdots \\
&\quad + a_r(b_0 + c_0) \text{ on applying axiom } (7) \text{ to each} \\
&\qquad \text{bracket,} \\
&= y_r.
\end{aligned}
$$

Hence the theorem is proved.   Q.E.D.

In these proofs it will have become apparent that many of the steps we take in algebraic calculations can be justified by appeal to the commutative, associative, and distributive laws. We began by assuming these for the arithmetic of the field F; we have now shown, by establishing (I') to (V'), that these same principles also hold for polynomials over F. This allows us to relax our vigilance somewhat. We now know that it is quite justified to assume for polynomials u, v, w that uv may be replaced by vu, that $u(v + w)$ may be multiplied out as $uv + uw$, that uvw has a meaning without any need for brackets.

We next proceed to put the theory into a more familiar form. We have already introduced the abbreviations,

> **1** for the sequence $(1, 0, 0, 0, \cdots)$,
> and x for $(0, 1, 0, 0, \cdots)$,
> and x^2 for $(0, 0, 1, 0, \cdots)$.

DEFINITION. x^n *stands for the sequence with* $p_n = 1$, *all other* p_i *zero*.

Note here that $p_r = 1$ refers to the element 1 of the field F. The n that occurs in p_n and x^n, however, is an ordinary counting number of our everyday arithmetic.

For instance, in the arithmetic modulo 5 with the elements O, I, II, III, IV, we still consider sequences such as (II, I, III, O, IV, II, I, O, O, $\cdots$) with $p_0 = $ II, $p_1 = $ I, $p_2 = $ III, $p_3 = $ O, $p_4 = $ IV, $p_5 = $ II, $p_6 = $ I, and we can consider II$\cdot$II$\cdot$II$\cdot$II$\cdot$II$\cdot$II$\cdot$II $= $ II^7. Thus, even though the arithmetic modulo 5 only contains the five distinct elements O, I, II, III, IV, yet the ordinary numbers, including the numbers 5, 6, 7, $\cdots$, cannot be kept entirely out of it. This might cause complications in the Pacific Island experiment (p. 18).

THEOREM. x^m P $x^n = x^{m+n}$.

Proof. Let x^m be $(p_0, p_1, p_2, \cdots)$ where $p_m = 1$, all other elements being zero.

Let x^n be $(q_0, q_1, q_2, \cdots)$ where $q_n = 1$, all other elements being zero.

If x^m P x^n is $(k_0, k_1, k_2, \cdots)$, then

$$k_r = \sum_{s=0}^{r} p_s q_{r-s}.$$

The term $p_s q_{r-s}$ will be zero if either p_s or q_{r-s} is zero. p_s is non-zero only for $s = m$, and q_{r-s} is non-zero only if $r - s = n$. Hence a non-zero term occurs on the right-hand side only if $s = m$ and $r - s = n$; that is, only if $r = m + n$. Hence k_r is zero except for $r = m + n$, and $k_{m+n} = 1$.

But $k_{m+n} = 1$, all other k_r zero is the sequence for x^{m+n}.

$\therefore$ x^m P $x^n = x^{m+n}$. Q.E.D.

THEOREM. *If a is any element of F, and $\mathbf{a}$ denotes the sequence $(a, 0, 0, 0, \cdots)$ then $\mathbf{a}$ P x^n is the sequence $(0, 0, \cdots, 0, a, 0, 0, \cdots)$; that is, ax^n is the sequence defined by $p_n = a$, all other $p_i = 0$.*

Proof. Calculate $\mathbf{a}$ P x^n. Verification is immediate.

THEOREM. *Every polynomial can be written in the form*

$$\mathbf{p}_0 \text{ S } (\mathbf{p}_1 \text{ P } x) \text{ S } (\mathbf{p}_2 \text{ P } x^2) \text{ S } \cdots \text{ S } (\mathbf{p}_n \text{ P } x^n).$$

The meaning of this theorem can be appreciated most easily if, for a moment, we replace S, the sum sign, by the usual $+$, and P, the product sign, by $\cdot$. The expression above then becomes

$$\mathbf{p_0} + \mathbf{p_1}\cdot x + \mathbf{p_2}\cdot x^2 + \cdots + \mathbf{p_n}\cdot x^n.$$

Proof. Since p_0 is $(p_0, 0, 0, 0, 0, \cdots)$, while by the previous theorem

$$\mathbf{p_1} \text{ P } x \text{ is } (0, p_1, 0, 0, 0, \cdots),$$
$$\mathbf{p_2} \text{ P } x^2 \text{ is } (0, 0, p_2, 0, 0, \cdots),$$

and so on, it is evident that $(p_0, p_1, p_2, p_3, \cdots, p_n, 0, 0, 0, \cdots)$ can be obtained by summing the terms above.
Q.E.D.

Thus, apart from the fact that the unfamiliar S and P are playing the parts of $+$ and $\cdot$, we have now reached a stage where polynomials can be written down in the ordinary way, and added and multiplied; we know that the commutative, associative, and distributive laws, (I′) through (V′), hold—that is to say, that the processes behave as in ordinary algebra.

There is, however, one remaining point. We seem now to have two distinct subjects. In terms of our machinery, we have one machine for adding and multiplying the elements of F—the numbers of the arithmetic. This is the old machine. The new machine deals only with sequences, with polynomials. The two machines seem quite distinct; no cables pass from one to the other. This seems a little peculiar, for surely an arithmetic and its algebra should be connected?

In our ordinary algebra we speak of a quadratic polynomial such as $4 + 3x + 2x^2$, a linear polynomial such as $4 + 3x$, and a *constant polynomial* such as 4. Thus, one and the same sign, 4, is used for the *number* 4 and the *constant polynomial* 4. Nor does this cause any trouble.

Most people in fact are hardly aware that any such distinction can be made. Probably this distinction is involved in the trouble that some students find in drawing the graph of $y = 4$. They seem to be helped by the suggestion that they should draw the graph of $y = 4 + 0 \cdot x$, which brings out the kinship of $y = 4$ to the family of lines $y = mx + c$, or reminds the student of the procedure for tabulating values and drawing the graph. The psychological effect of writing $y = 4$ as $y = 4 + 0 \cdot x$ seems to lie in emphasizing that 4 can be regarded as a particular case of a polynomial.

How does this overlapping of number behavior and polynomial behavior appear on our machines? Let a and b be any elements of F. On the arithmetic machine, we can find $a + b$ and $a \cdot b$. What will happen if, on the polynomial machine, we find **a S b** and **a P b**?

$$\textbf{a} \text{ is } (a, 0, 0, 0, \cdots).$$
$$\textbf{b} \text{ is } (b, 0, 0, 0, \cdots).$$

The rules for S and P give

$$\textbf{a S b} \text{ is } (a + b, 0, 0, 0, \cdots).$$
$$\textbf{a P b} \text{ is } (ab, 0, 0, 0, \cdots).$$

Thus

$$\textbf{a S b} = (\textbf{a} + \textbf{b}),$$
$$\textbf{a P b} = (\textbf{ab}).$$

For example,

$$2 \text{ S } 3 = 5,$$
$$2 \text{ P } 3 = 6.$$

This means to say, we can do our arithmetic on the algebra machine.

$2 \text{ S } 3 = 5$ means that the polynomial 2 added to the polynomial 3 gives the polynomial 5; this runs exactly parallel to the relation between *numbers*, $2 + 3 = 5$. This parallelism is an example of *isomorphism*. The structure, the pattern, of numbers is exactly the same as the structure, the pattern, of constant polynomials.

Accordingly, it becomes something of a luxury to own both a polynomial machine and an arithmetic machine. Since we can do all our calculations on the polynomial machine, we can trade our arithmetic machine in. Whenever we want to do an arithmetical calculation about numbers a, b, c, we can set up the polynomials $(a, 0, 0, \cdots)$, $(b, 0, 0, \cdots)$, $(c, 0, 0, \cdots)$ and infer the arithmetical result from operations on the polynomial machine.

Getting rid of the arithmetic machine is welcome. We have so far had to use S, P, and $+$, $\cdot$ to avoid confusion between operations on polynomials (sequences) and operations on numbers. But now that the arithmetic machine has gone, there is no longer a need for this distinction. We can write the familiar $+$ where S stood on the machine, and $\cdot$ for P. We can also drop the distinction between the number a and the constant polynomial **a**.

In effect, the sequences $(p_0, p_1, p_2, \cdots)$ and the operations S and P are now relegated to the interior of the machine. On the outside of the machine we see (if ordinary numbers compose the field F) 0, 1, 2, 3, and so on; $+$ and $\cdot$; x, x^2, x^3, and so on.

If we press $4 + 3 \cdot x + 2 \cdot x^2$, then, in some space inside the machine, the sequence $(4, 3, 2, 0, 0, 0, \cdots)$ will appear. If we simply press 4, the sequence will be $(4, 0, 0, 0, \cdots)$. When the operation $+$ is required, the machine carries out S in its interior; when $\cdot$ is required, the machine carries out P.

Note that x has not changed its meaning at all. When we press x, the machine sets up $(0, 1, 0, 0, 0, \cdots)$ in its interior. That is all we know about x. There is no requirement that x be an element of F, a number, or anything of that sort.

Substituting a Value for x

Have we perhaps gone too far? After all, we still want to say that $x^2 - 3x + 2 = 0$ if $x = 1$ or $x = 2$. What are we to do when we want to substitute $x = 2$ or $x = k$ in a polynomial $p_0 + p_1 x + \cdots + p_n x^n$?

x^m has been defined by the sequence $(0, 0, 0, \cdots , 0, 1, 0, 0, 0, \cdots)$ that it produces in the machine. However, the theorem we had earlier, which we now write $x^m \cdot x^n = x^{m+n}$ gives us another way of regarding x^m.

We have seen earlier that $x^2 = x \cdot x$. Hence

$$x^3 = x^{1+2} = x \cdot x^2 = x \cdot x \cdot x,$$
$$x^4 = x^{1+3} = x \cdot x^3 = x \cdot x \cdot x \cdot x,$$

and so on. The cubic polynomial

$$a + b \cdot x + c \cdot x^2 + d \cdot x^3$$

could thus be written

$$a + b \cdot x + c \cdot x \cdot x + d \cdot x \cdot x \cdot x.$$

In what relation does this stand to the expression

$$a + b \cdot k + c \cdot k \cdot k + d \cdot k \cdot k \cdot k,$$

where k is an element of F?

Let us think what happens in the interior of the machine when these two things are calculated:

$$\begin{array}{ll} a \text{ produces} & (a, 0, 0, 0, 0, 0, 0, \cdots), \\ b \cdot x \text{ produces} & (0, b, 0, 0, 0, 0, 0, \cdots), \\ c \cdot x \cdot x \text{ produces} & (0, 0, c, 0, 0, 0, 0, \cdots), \\ d \cdot x \cdot x \cdot x \text{ produces} & (0, 0, 0, d, 0, 0, 0, \cdots). \end{array}$$

Summing $a + b \cdot x + c \cdot x \cdot x + d \cdot x \cdot x \cdot x$ produces $(a, b, c, d, 0, 0, 0, \cdots)$ as, of course, we could have foreseen. On the other hand,

$$a \text{ produces } \quad (a, 0, 0, 0, 0, 0, 0, \cdots),$$
$$b \cdot k \text{ produces } \quad (bk, 0, 0, 0, 0, 0, 0, \cdots),$$
$$c \cdot k \cdot k \text{ produces } \quad (ck^2, 0, 0, 0, 0, 0, 0, \cdots),$$
$$d \cdot k \cdot k \cdot k \text{ produces } \quad (dk^3, 0, 0, 0, 0, 0, 0, \cdots).$$

Summing $a + b \cdot k + c \cdot k \cdot k + d \cdot k \cdot k \cdot k$ produces

$$(a + bk + ck^2 + dk^3, 0, 0, 0, 0, 0, 0, \cdots).$$

It will be convenient to use the abbreviation $f(x)$ for $a + b \cdot x + c \cdot x \cdot x + d \cdot x \cdot x \cdot x$, and $f(k)$ for $a + b \cdot k + c \cdot k \cdot k + d \cdot k \cdot k \cdot k$.

These look very much alike, but they appear very differently on the machine. $f(x)$ appears as $(a, b, c, d, 0, 0, 0, \cdots)$, a polynomial of degree three, specified by the four elements a, b, c, d of F. $f(k)$ appears as $(e, 0, 0, 0, 0, 0, \cdots)$, where $e = a + b \cdot k + c \cdot k \cdot k + d \cdot k \cdot k \cdot k$ is a single element of F. We can regard $f(k)$ as a constant polynomial or, if we like, we can identify it with the element e of F; we agreed earlier to neglect the distinction between **e**, the constant polynomial $(e, 0, 0, 0, \cdots)$ and the element e of F.

In ordinary high school algebra we meet the idea of "substituting k for x." On our calculating machine we accordingly must introduce a key marked, "substitute k for x."

If the calculating machine is carrying the sequence $(a, b, c, d, 0, 0, 0, \cdots)$ which represents $f(x)$, and we press the "substitute k for x" key, the machine will compute $e = a + bk + ck^2 + dk^3$—this is a single number, an element of F—and will set up the sequence $(e, 0, 0, 0, 0, 0, \cdots)$.

This explains and defines what we mean by "substitute k for x." If on a machine you see a knob marked with an unfamiliar word, and you want to understand the meaning of this word, all you need do is turn the knob and observe what happens in the machine. When you are completely familiar with what this knob *does*, then you understand the word written on it. There is nothing more to understand.

I emphasize this because there is much discussion at present of the correct use of words. People are worried about whether they really understand what a word means. Some philosophers hold that successful thinking is only possible after all words have been defined exactly. It may be that some people actually do think by means of words. If so, they are a minority. Most people think by imagining, by picturing actual objects, actual processes, actual happenings. We speak to each other in order to make sure that we are thinking of the same thing and picturing it in the same way. We clear up confusion in our own minds by thinking about something until we have a clear picture of it.

The idea that a word or a symbol has one fixed, exact meaning is dangerous even in mathematics. Poincaré, one of the greatest modern mathematicians, declared "Mathematics is the art of calling different things by the same name." We have had an example of this already. We used $+$ originally in arithmetic with $3 + 4 = 7$. When we got to dealing with the arithmetic modulo 5, we could have brought in a new sign of combination and written, perhaps, $III \oplus IV = II$. But we found it more convenient to write $3 + 4 = 2$. 2, 3, 4, and $+$ all have new meanings here, but we find it convenient to use the same signs. When we were dealing with sequences, we used a new sign S for sum, 3 for $(3, 0, 0, 0, \cdots)$, and 4 for $(4, 0, 0, 0, 0, \cdots)$. We were glad, though, when we stopped writing $3 \mathrm{S} 4 = 7$ and went back to $3 + 4 = 7$ for constant polynomials. So we have already used $+$ in three different senses. When we use a sign, then, it does not imply that all its meanings are exactly the same, but that there is enough

in common to make the family resemblance wortl
emphasizing.

I should certainly not advise anyone teaching
ninth-grade algebra to say that x is the sequence
$(0, 1, 0, 0, 0, \cdots)$.

Earlier we discussed the question of the polynomia
$x^2 + x$ over F, the field consisting of 0, 1 modulo 2. Wa:
this polynomial equal to zero or not? We have two set
of facts:

(i) The polynomial $x^2 + x$ is the sequence $(0, 1, 1, 0$
$0, 0, \cdots)$. The constant polynomial 0 is the sequenc•
$(0, 0, 0, 0, 0, 0, \cdots)$. These two sequences are distinct
In this sense, $x^2 + x \neq 0$.

(ii) If in $x^2 + x$ we substitute 0 for x, we get $0^2 + 0$
that is, 0. If we substitute 1 for x we get $1^2 + 1$, whicl
is also 0. 0 and 1 are the only elements of F. Hence fo
every k of F, $k^2 + k = 0$.

It is desirable that we should have some way of indi
cating whether we are posing questions, or makinç
statements, in the sense of (i) or (ii). We might mak•
some sort of convention about the use of letters; w•
might always use x for sense (i), and k for sense (ii)
This might be inconvenient at times; it is surprising hov
soon the letters of the alphabet get used up in a mathe
matical discussion.

It is better to have some terminology to indicate hov
a symbol is being used. When we write $k^2 + k = 0$ t•
mean that if any element of F is added to its square, th
result is zero, we say that k is *a variable*. When we writ
$x^2 + x$ without caring what x may mean or whether i
means anything at all, simply as a symbol obeying cer
tain formal rules, we say that x is *an indeterminate*.

A professor of mathematics once made the followin
criticism of the remainder theorem. He said, "The re

mainder theorem states that when $f(x)$ is divided by
$x - a$, the remainder is $f(a)$. But when $x = a$, $x - a$ is
zero. You cannot divide by zero. That means we cannot
consider x being a when we are dividing by $x - a$. The
proofs of the remainder theorem that depend on a being
substituted for x are therefore false."

This criticism is entirely incorrect. The critic is clearly
thinking of x as a *variable*, so that x is a number and
$x - a$ is also a number. Let us take an example of division and see how well or badly it works to regard x as
a variable.

Example. "When x^2 is divided by $x - 3$, the quotient
is $x + 3$ and the remainder 9." I am sure you will agree
that this is a correct statement. Let us see how it looks
when we take particular numbers for x.

$x = 5$. "When 25 is divided by 2, the quotient is 8
and the remainder 9."

$x = 6$. "When 36 is divided by 3, the quotient is 9
and the remainder 9."

$x = 7$. "When 49 is divided by 4, the quotient is 10
and the remainder 9."

There is a sense in which all of these are true. For
instance, $25 = 2 \times 8 + 9$. Yet they represent very
strange arithmetic.

If, purely as a matter of arithmetic, we had been asked
to divide 25 by 2, 36 by 3, and 49 by 4, we would have
given the remainders as 1, 0, 1, respectively. We could
never have arrived at the conclusion "The remainder is
always 9" by arithmetical experiments.

In fact, the sentence "When x^2 is divided by $x - 3$,
the remainder is 9" is a statement of algebra that is *not*
a generalization about arithmetic. The division in question is not arithmetical division: it is division according
to the rules we learn for dealing with polynomials.

"Divide x^2 by $x - 3$" means exactly the same a "divide $(0, 0, 1, 0, 0, 0, \cdots)$ by $(-3, 1, 0, 0, 0, \cdots)$." It does not make sense in any other interpretation.

The thing we are dividing by here is $(-3, 1, 0, 0, 0, \cdots)$, and this is not zero. Zero is $(0, 0, 0, 0, 0, \cdots)$. There is no need to take precautions to ensure that the divisor does not become zero. $(-3, 1, 0, 0, 0, \cdots)$ just is not $(0, 0, 0, 0, 0, \cdots)$, and there are no circumstances in which it could become $(0, 0, 0, \cdots)$. A polynomial can always be divided by $x - 3$ in the sense in which long division is done in algebra.

The distinction between x regarded as a variable and x regarded as an indeterminate is therefore not an empty one.

We do have to distinguish between the two statements below.

Statement I. For the *indeterminate* x, the polynomial $f(x) = 0$. This means that $f(x)$ is $(0, 0, 0, \cdots)$. This statement is true, for instance, if $f(x) = -x^2 + 1 + (x - 1)(x + 1)$. When this $f(x)$ is simplified by the rules of algebra, the result is zero. We could express it as $(1, 0, -1, 0, 0, 0, \cdots)$ S $(-1, 1, 0, 0, \cdots)$ P $(1, 1, 0, 0, 0, \cdots) = (0, 0, 0, 0, \cdots)$.

Statement II. For all values of the *variable* x, the polynomial $f(x) = 0$. This means that, for every element k of the field F, we have $f(k) = 0$.

What is the relationship between statement I and statement II? We have seen that statement II is true with F the arithmetic modulo 2, for $x^2 + x$. But statement I is not true for $x^2 + x$, since $x^2 + x$ is $(0, 1, 1, 0, 0, \cdots)$ and not $(0, 0, 0, 0, 0, \cdots)$. So statement I does not follow from statement II, at least not for every field F. (It does follow in elementary algebra, as we noted earlier.)

Does statement II follow from statement I? If state

ment I is true, $f(x)$ is $(0, 0, 0, 0, 0, 0, \cdots)$. Now $(0, 0, 0, 0, 0, 0, \cdots)$ is a particular case of $(a, b, c, d, 0, 0, \cdots)$ with $a = 0$, $b = 0$, $c = 0$, $d = 0$. I have quite arbitrarily chosen to regard $(0, 0, 0, 0, 0, \cdots)$ as a cubic, in order to make clear that we are not involved in a discussion of the infinite series $0 + 0k + 0k^2 + 0k^3 + 0k^4 + \cdots$. A polynomial is essentially a finite sequence. In the language of page 42, it may be "4, 3, 2, finish." "Finish" means that we have reached the stage where we have zeros only. $(0, 0, 0, 0, 0, \cdots)$ could be written "finish"; with it we finish before we start! This makes the interpretation of the procedure for substituting k slightly obscure. If, however, we regard $(0, 0, 0, 0, 0, \cdots)$ as "0, 0, 0, 0, finish," which we are entitled to do, we can apply the rule without any difficulties of interpretation. The explanation of "Substitute k for x" given on page 61 leads to the value $e = a + bk + ck^2 + dk^3 = 0 + 0k + 0k^2 + 0k^3 = 0$, whatever element of F the quantity k may be. Hence, statement II follows from statement I.

There is an important point to notice. The explanation of "substitute k for x" assumed that $f(x)$ had been obtained in the standard form, $p_0 + p_1x + p_2x^2 + \cdots + p_nx^n$. Substituting k for x gave $p_0 + p_1k + p_2k^2 + \cdots + p_nk^n$.

If we were given $f(x)$, say in the form

$$f(x) = (a_0 + a_1x + a_2x^2)(b_0 + b_1x + b_2x^2),$$

the definition instructs us to multiply out $f(x)$ as $(a_0, a_1, a_2, 0, 0, 0, \cdots)$ P $(b_0, b_1, b_2, 0, 0, 0, \cdots) = (a_0b_0, a_0b_1 + a_1b_0, a_0b_2 + a_1b_1 + a_2b_0, a_1b_2 + a_2b_1, a_2b_2, 0, 0, 0, \cdots)$,

and then to press the key "Substitute k for x," giving $f(k) = a_0b_0 + (a_0b_1 + a_1b_0) k + (a_0b_2 + a_1b_1 + a_2b_0) k^2 + (a_1b_2 + a_2b_1) k^3 + a_2b_2k^4$.

But you naturally ask, "Could we not use the simpler form $(a_0 + a_1k + a_2k^2)(b_0 + b_1k + b_2k^2)$?" The suggestion is that multiplying out and then substituting could be replaced by substituting and then multiplying out. For instance, the two procedures for substituting 3 for x in $(x - 1)(x + 1)$ would be

(i) $(x - 1)(x + 1) = x^2 - 1$.
   Substituting 3 for x gives $3^2 - 1 = 8$.

(ii) Substituting 3 for x in $(x - 1)$ gives 2.
   Substituting 3 for x in $(x + 1)$ gives 4. $2 \cdot 4 = 8$.

Procedure (i) we know to be correct, for it merely carries out the instructions of the definition. Procedure (ii) we observe, in this example, gives the same answer as procedure (i).

Now, of course, it is not surprising that this should be so. If you will look back to page 34, you will see that we obtained our rules for constructing the polynomial machine by considering what happens when we add and multiply in elementary algebra. The process of our thought has been something like this.

(I) We learn arithmetic.

(II) We notice in arithmetic various facts, such as $3 \times 4 = 4 \times 3$ and $3 + 4 = 4 + 3$. We satisfy ourselves that these facts are particular examples of general properties of numbers, expressed by axioms (*1*) through (*12*). The numbers of arithmetic form a field.

(III) The processes of elementary algebra can be justified by the field axioms. For instance, if a, b, c, d are elements of a field F, we can show that

$$(a + bk) + (c + dk) = (a + c) + (b + d)k$$

and

$$(a + bk)(c + dk) = ac + (ad + bc)k + bdk^2$$

for any element k of the field F.

(IV) We extract from (III) the abstract pattern

$$(a, b, 0, 0, \cdots) \ S \ (c, d, 0, 0, \cdots)$$
$$= (a + c, b + d, 0, 0, \cdots),$$

$(a, b, 0, 0, \cdots)$ P $(c, d, 0, 0, \cdots)$
$$= (ac, ad + bc, bd, 0, 0, \cdots),$$

and specify, quite abstractly, our polynomial machine for combining sequences by the operations S and P.

(V) By introducing the sign x for the sequence $(0, 1, 0, 0, \cdots)$, and slipping back into writing $+$ for S and $\cdot$ for P, we are able to write the equations of (IV) in the form

$$(a + bx) + (c + dx) = (a + c) + (b + d)x,$$
$$(a + bx)(c + dx) = ac + (bc + ad)x + bdx^2,$$

which look very much like the equations of (III). What we have gained is that x is no longer restricted to being a number, an element of the field F.

(VI) We verify that the sequences of (IV), and consequently their expressions in the symbolism of (V), obey the commutative, associative, and distributive laws, and hence can be worked with in exactly the same way as the expressions of elementary algebra.

(VII) The operations of (IV) and (V) have been based on the patterns of (III). This means that, although the symbol x does not *have* to be interpreted as an element of the field F, yet it *can* be so interpreted. If, in any true statement of (V), x is everywhere replaced by k, an element of the field F, we obtain a true statement in the language of (III).

The assertion (VII) may be illustrated by the following two theorems.

THEOREM. *If $p(x)$, $q(x)$, $f(x)$ are polynomials in the indeterminate x over a field F, and $p(x) + q(x) = f(x)$, then for any element k of F, $p(k) + q(k) = f(k)$.*

THEOREM. *If $p(x)$, $q(x)$, $g(x)$ are polynomials in the indeterminate x over a field F, and $p(x) \cdot q(x) = f(x)$, then for any element k of F, $p(k) \cdot q(k) = f(k)$.*

By combining these theorems, we can obtain results

such as this: if

$$f(x) = p(x)\ q(x) + r(x)$$

for an indeterminate x, then

$$f(k) = p(k)\ q(k) + r(k)$$

for any element k of F.

EXERCISES

1. Write out the proof of the remainder theorem. When any equation is written, make it plain whether the symbols are indeterminates, variables, or fixed elements of a field F. State explicitly any theorems used in the course of the proof.

2. $ax^2 + bx + c$ is a quadratic over a field F in an indeterminate x. Explain what is meant by saying that the quadratic has at most two roots. Prove that this statement is correct whatever the field F.

Chapter 3

Finite Arithmetics

EARLIER we considered the arithmetic of Even and Odd. This was a particular example of an arithmetic modulo n, namely the arithmetic modulo 2. When we were discussing Even and Odd, we accepted many statements such as "Even plus Odd equals Odd" as agreeing with our experience of arithmetic. We did not analyze or prove these results. To prove them is, of course, simply a matter of elementary algebra. We now look at these proofs as a first step toward proving the properties of the arithmetic modulo n.

"Even plus Odd equals Odd" is a short way of saying, "When any even number is added to any odd number, the result is an odd number." To prove the truth of this statement we must translate into algebraic symbolism the expressions "even number" and "odd number."

If our symbols $a, b, c, \cdots, x, y, z$ stand for integers, the numbers $2a, 2b, 2c, \cdots$, are *even*; the numbers $2a + 1$, $2b + 1, 2c + 1, \cdots$, are *odd*. Any even number can be expressed as $2a$. Any odd number can be expressed as $2b + 1$. When these are added, we get $2a + 2b + 1 = 2(a + b) + 1$, hence an odd number; and we have proved the statement.

There is no difficulty in justifying the other results of the addition table modulo 2.

The multiplication table is justified by the following four results:

$$(2a) \cdot (2b) = 2(2ab),$$
$$(2a) \cdot (2b + 1) = 2 \cdot a(2b + 1),$$
$$(2a + 1) \cdot 2b = 2 \cdot b(2a + 1),$$
$$(2a + 1) \cdot (2b + 1) = 2(2ab + a + b) + 1.$$

Apart from the particular results obtained, such as "Odd times Odd equals Odd," this procedure shows that the question "When an odd number is multiplied by an odd number, is the result Odd or Even?" has a definite answer. We do not need to ask, "Which odd numbers are you thinking of?"

Compare the situation if we divide numbers up into perfect squares and other numbers. One cannot answer "yes" or "no" to the question, "When a square number is added to a square number, is the result square?" $0 + 1$, $9 + 16$, $25 + 144$ are examples of results that are squares; $1 + 4$, $1 + 9$, $4 + 9$ are examples of results that are not.

Our procedure then, in forming the arithmetic modulo 2 (and the other modular arithmetics), has been to divide the integers up into classes in such a way that, if we know to which classes x and y belong, we know to which classes $x + y$ and xy belong.

The arithmetic modulo 2 is easy to talk about because we have two generally accepted words, Even and Odd, to describe the classes. The language does not contain words to express that a number is divisible by 3, or leaves remainder 1 or remainder 2 on division by 3. We accordingly have to invent symbols such as

O to label any number of the form $3a$,

I to label any number of the form $3a + 1$,

II to label any number of the form $3a + 2$.

Similarly, we used the symbols O, I, II, III, IV for the arithmetic modulo 5.

For example, to prove that III·IV = II modulo 5, means to prove that $(5a + 3)(5b + 4)$ is of the form $5c + 2$, which is very easy to do. We thus show (i) that when a number x from class III is multiplied by a number y from class IV the product xy lies in a definite class, independent of the particular numbers x and y chosen; (ii) that the class is in fact the class II.

Of these results, (ii) is, so to speak, arithmetical. It holds for arithmetic modulo 5, but not necessarily for other arithmetics; for instance, in modulo 7 arithmetic, III·IV = V.

Result (i), however, has no reference to particular numbers, and generalizes immediately to give theorem 1.

THEOREM 1. *If, for any whole number n, the integers are divided into classes, so that class P contains all numbers of the form $na + p$, class Q contains all numbers of the form $na + q$, and so on; then, given only that the numbers x and y belong to the classes X and Y, the classes to which $x + y$ and xy belong are determined.*

We can restate this result as follows: if x_1 and x_2 are in the same class, and y_1 and y_2 are in the same class, then $x_1 + y_1$ and $x_2 + y_2$ are in the same class, and x_1y_1 and x_2y_2 are in the same class.

Saying that x_1 and x_2 are in the same class is equivalent to saying that $x_1 - x_2$ is a multiple of n.

Thus we are given $x_1 = nc + x_2$, $y_1 = nd + y_2$.

Hence $x_1 + y_1 = n(c + d) + x_2 + y_2$ and $(x_1 + y_1) - (x_2 + y_2)$ is a multiple of n.

Also $x_1y_1 = n^2cd + ncy_2 + ndx_2 + x_2y_2$ so $x_1y_1 - x_2y_2$ is a multiple of n.

The theorem is proved.   Q.E.D.

We have now shown that axioms (1) and (2) hold for arithmetic modulo n. We have defined $X + Y$ and $X \cdot Y$;

namely, if x is any number of the class X, and y any number of the class Y, then $X + Y$ means the class to which $x + y$ belongs, and $X \cdot Y$ the class to which xy belongs. Theorem 1 assures us that this definition is consistent.

Axioms (3), (4), (5), (6), (7) are now almost self-evident.

Axiom (3) requires $X + Y = Y + X$. Now $Y + X$ is the class containing $y + x$, while $X + Y$ is the class containing $x + y$. But we know, for any numbers x, y, that $y + x = x + y$. Call this number k. Then $X + Y$ is the class containing k, and $Y + X$ is the class containing k. Hence $X + Y$ and $Y + X$ are the same class.   Q.E.D.

Axioms (4), (5), (6), (7) follow in the same way. If Z is the class containing z, axiom (7), for instance, requires $X \cdot (Y + Z) = (X \cdot Y) + (X \cdot Z)$. We show that $X \cdot (Y + Z)$ is the class containing $x(y + z)$, and $(X \cdot Y) + (X \cdot Z)$ is the class containing $xy + xz$. As the numbers are the same, the classes are the same.

Axiom (8), on subtraction, asserts that, for given classes P, Q (containing the numbers p, q) the equation

$$P + X = Q$$

has one and only one solution. It evidently has a solution. For let S be the class containing the number $(q - p)$. Then $P + S$ is the class containing $p + (q - p)$, that is, $P + S$ contains q. $\therefore P + S = Q$. $\therefore S$ is a solution.

Suppose the class T, containing the number t, is also a solution. $P + T$ is the class containing $p + t$. If $P + T = Q$, this means that $p + t$ belongs to Q. $\therefore p + t = q + na$ for some whole number a. $t = (q - p) + na$. Hence t belongs to the class S. $\therefore$ The class to which t belongs is S. That is, T is S.

Axiom (8) is thus proved to hold.

Axiom (9) asserts that there is a class playing the role

of zero. Let O be the class containing the number 0. $P + O$ is the class containing the number $p + 0$. As $p + 0 = p$, $P + O = P$. Hence O plays the role of zero. By axiom (8), there can only be one such class. Otherwise the subtraction $P - P$ would have more than one answer.

We may as well deal with axiom (11) now. It should be evident that the class I, containing the number 1, plays the role of unity.

Axioms (10) and (12) do not hold for all modular arithmetics. For instance, in arithmetic modulo 6, the equation $II \cdot X = III$ has no solution, so division is not possible. Also $II \cdot III = O$; axiom (12) does not hold in this arithmetic.

The class O contains all numbers of the form $na + 0$, that is, all numbers na, all multiples of n. Thus "$XY = O$ only if $X = O$ or $Y = O$" is the same requirement as "xy is a multiple of n only if x is a multiple of n or y is a multiple of n." This property is characteristic of prime n.

Hence axiom (12) holds if and only if n is prime.

Does axiom (10) hold when n is prime? That is to say, given classes P, Q, where P is not O, can we find a class X such that $P \cdot X = Q$?

How do we go about finding such an X in practice? For example, in the arithmetic modulo 5, how should we solve $II \cdot X = III$? We should have to look through the II times table until we found the answer III. Here is the two times table.

$$II \cdot O = O$$
$$II \cdot I = II$$
$$II \cdot II = IV$$
$$II \cdot III = I$$
$$II \cdot IV = III$$

If you look at the right-hand side, you will see that all the classes O, I, II, III, IV occur there. That is to say, we may make $\text{II} \cdot X$ equal to any class we like, by choosing X suitably. In arithmetic modulo 5 then, division by II is always possible.

This suggests a way of studying the arithmetic modulo n. This contains n classes, corresponding to the numbers $0, 1, 2, \cdots, (n-1)$. We take some class P, and let X run through the n classes. If the resulting PX are all different, they must form a complete set of classes. By choosing X suitably, we can make $PX = Q$ for any assigned Q. Division by P is then possible.

Can we show then that, when P is not O, all the PX are different? We suppose, of course, that n is prime; it is easily seen that for n composite the result is not true.

The proof is extremely simple. It almost leaps to the eye as soon as we state the question in algebraic symbols.

Suppose the PX are not all distinct. Then $X = U$ and $X = V$ give the same result; that is $PU = PV$. But (in view of the axioms already proved) this means $P(U - V) = \text{O}$. But P is not O, by our assumptions. $U - V$ is not O, since U and V are not equal. Axiom (12) has already been established. Hence $P(U - V)$ is not O, since neither factor is O. We thus arrive at a contradiction if we assume the PX not distinct. Hence the PX are distinct.

Accordingly, when n is prime, division is possible, for divisors other than O. We have thus theorem 2.

THEOREM 2. *The arithmetic modulo n, where n is prime, is a field.*

For this arithmetic satisfies axioms (1)–(12).

You may have noticed that we proved axiom (10) from axiom (12) and the remaining axioms. It is evident that there is a close connection between axioms (10) and (12). Since we proved axiom (10) from axiom (12), have we perhaps not been extravagant in including axiom (10) at all? Could we not simply assume (12) and deduce (10)?

For a finite field—that is, a field with a finite number of elements—we could do so. But consider a very familiar structure, the integers. For the integers, axioms (*1*) through (*9*), (*11*), (*12*) hold. All the answers in the two times table are distinct:

$$-6, -4, -2, 0, 2, 4, 6, \cdots.$$

But this does not prove that every number occurs as an answer in the two times table. In fact, $2x = 3$ has no solution in integers.

Thus for the integers, axiom (*12*) holds, but (*10*) is false. It is thus impossible to deduce axiom (*10*) from (*12*), the other axioms being given, without the additional information that the structure contains only a finite number of elements. And most of our algebra, of course, deals with structures having an infinity of elements. For such a structure, axiom (*10*) is a stronger assumption than (*12*).

Question: If axioms (*1*) through (*11*) are given, does Axiom (*12*) follow?

An Alternative Approach to Division

Our proof of axiom (*10*) has two limitations. First of all, a proof has two functions. One is to establish the particular result. This, of course, our proof does. The other function is to throw light on similar problems, to suggest analogies. Our proof holds only for finite structures. For infinite structures it is, if anything, misleading.

Second, our proof shows that $PX = Q$ has a solution, but it does not offer us any convenient way of calculating that solution. We are assured that, if we try the n possible values of X, we shall find a solution among them. Our work will not be wasted; but if n is at all large, we may have a lot of work to do.

An alternative approach is possible, which both enables us to calculate X and sheds light on related problems. It leads us to a theorem that does not appear very extraordinary, but which in fact is of great importance. This alternative approach is through a process that you will find in the older arithmetic textbooks for finding the highest common factor, or H.C.F. (The H.C.F. is also known as the greatest common divisor, or G.C.D.) Suppose the H.C.F. of 481 and 689 is required. The work is set out as follows:

$$
\begin{array}{c c c c}
2 & 481 & 689 & 1 \\
  & 416 & 481 & \\
\hline
5 & 65 & 208 & 3 \\
  & 65 & 195 & \\
\hline
  & 0 & 13 & \\
\end{array}
$$

The two numbers 481 and 689 are first written down. We divide 481 into 689. It goes once and leaves remainder 208. We divide this remainder into 481. It goes twice, and leaves 65. This remainder 65 is then divided into 208. It goes three times and leaves 13. Finally 13 divides 65. It goes exactly five times. The remainder 0 has now been reached, and the process terminates. The last number reached before zero, namely 13 here, is the H.C.F. As $481 = 37 \times 13$ and $689 = 53 \times 13$, this result is correct for this example.

Of course, with different initial numbers, the process may run to different lengths. We will justify the process in the particular case in which it follows the pattern above. It is easy to see that the ideas of this proof apply equally well in the general case.

Suppose, then, that we begin with two numbers a, b and obtain the following scheme.

n	a	b	m
	nc	ma	
	——	——	
q	d	c	p
	qe	pd	
	——	——	
	0	e	

This is equivalent to the following equations.

$$b - ma = c \tag{1}$$
$$a - nc = d \tag{2}$$
$$c - pd = e \tag{3}$$
$$d - qe = 0 \tag{4}$$

We want to prove that e is the H.C.F. of a and b; that is, we want to show that a and b are multiples of e, and that no number larger than e is a factor of both a and b.

From equation (4), d is a multiple of e.

From equation (3), $c = pd + e$, so c is a multiple of e.

From equation (2), $a = nc + d$. As c and d are both multiples of e, so is a.

From equation (1), $b = ma + c$. As a and c are multiples of e, so is b. This establishes that a and b are multiples of e. Now suppose that some number k is a factor of both a and b.

Equation (1) shows that k is also a factor of c. As k is a factor of a and c, equation (2) shows that k is a factor of d. Then equation (3) shows that k is a factor of e.

Hence any common factor k of a and b is a factor of e. It is thus impossible that k should be larger than e. Hence e is the H.C.F. of a and b.   Q.E.D.

We can draw a further consequence from these equations. In equation (3) we can substitute for d from equation (2). This gives

$$e = c - p(a - nc) = c(1 + pn) - pa.$$

In this equation we can substitute for c from equation (1).

$$e = (1 + pn)(b - ma) - pa$$
$$= (1 + pn)b - a(m + pmn + p).$$

Thus e has been expressed in the form $ax + by$ where x and y are integers. It does not disturb us that x happens to be negative.

The letter h is frequently used for the H.C.F. Using this notation, we have the important theorem 3.

THEOREM 3. *If h is the H.C.F. of the integers a, b, there exist integers x, y such that*

$$h = ax + by.$$

For example, the numbers 31 and 40 have H.C.F. 1. Thus it must be possible to find whole numbers x, y for which

$$31x + 40y = 1.$$

To find these by trial and error would not be too easy. If we carry out the H.C.F. process and apply the argument used above, we find that $x = -9$, $y = 7$ is a solution. (Other solutions also exist.)

EXERCISES

1. Find integers x, y to satisfy (i) $3x + 5y = 1$, (ii) $8x + 13y = 1$, (iii) $17x + 12y = 1$.

2. Could there be integers x, y for which $4x + 6y = 1$?

3. What is the necessary and sufficient condition that k must satisfy if $ax + by = k$ is to have a solution in integers x, y? a, b are given integers.

We are now in a position to deal with the question of division in the arithmetic modulo n, with n prime.

If, as before, P and Q stand for the classes to which given numbers p and q belong, solving $PX = Q$ is equivalent to finding a number x such that px is in class Q. This means that, for some a, $px = na + q$. Conversely, if we can find numbers x, a to satisfy this last equation, then $PX = Q$ for the class X containing x.

Now n is prime. p is not a multiple of n, for that would mean $P = O$. The only factors of n are 1 and n itself. Since n is not a factor of p, the H.C.F. of n and p must be 1. Accordingly, by Theorem 3, we can find integers u, v for which $pu + nv = 1$.

Multiply this equation by q.

Hence

$$puq + nvq = q.$$

Let

$$x = uq, \ a = -vq.$$

Then

$$px - na = q.$$

Hence $PX = Q$ as required. Note that, if u belongs to the class U,

$$PU = \text{I}.$$

In the modulo n, arithmetic, U is I/P, the reciprocal of P. Theorem 3 has in effect enabled us to show that every class P has a reciprocal I/P. If we multiply this reciprocal by Q, we arrive at Q/P, the desired quotient.

EXERCISES

1. In the arithmetic modulo 17, find the reciprocals of 7 and 11.

2. In the arithmetic modulo 257, find the reciprocals of 43 and 16.

3. In the arithmetic modulo 11, simplify the fractions 2/7 and 5/6.

The calculations above are simply intended to help you to fix the content of theorem 3 in your mind. Needless to say, it is the light this theorem throws on general theory that is important, not its use in calculations such as question 2 above. We rarely need to perform calculations of this type.

Note that the proof above makes no mention of the finiteness of the structure. The line of thought here followed proves fruitful in connection with infinite fields, as we shall see.

Chapter 4

An Analogy Between Integers and Polynomials

THERE ARE many resemblances between the integers $\cdots, -5, -4, -3, -2, -1, 0, 1, 2, 3, \cdots$, and the polynomials $a, bx + c, dx^2 + ex + f, \cdots$, where $a, b, c, d, e, f, \cdots$, stand for rational numbers. Actually, I do not have to insist on the coefficients $a, b, c, \cdots$, being rational numbers. They could be chosen from any field without harming the analogy. I specify the rational field in order that we may have something definite and familiar.

The resemblance will become apparent if you run through axioms (1)–(12), and see which of them are true for our polynomials. If you add two polynomials, the result is a polynomial. If you multiply two polynomials, the result is a polynomial. Thus axioms (1) and (2) hold. Axioms (3) through (7), the familiar laws of algebra, certainly hold. Axiom (8) holds; subtraction can be done with polynomials. Axiom (9) holds; when you subtract a polynomial from itself you get zero. Axiom (10) does *not* hold. $x/(x + 1)$ is not a polynomial. Axiom (11) does hold; 1 is a polynomial. Axiom (12) also holds; if a product of polynomials is zero, one factor must be

zero. Here, of course, "a polynomial is zero" means that
the polynomial is $0 + 0x + 0x^2$. Axiom (*12*) amounts to
saying that, when you start out to multiply, say, $x - 1$
and $x + 1$, neither of which is zero, you can be sure that
the product will not be $0 + 0x + 0x^2$. The product is,
of course, $x^2 - 1$. You are speaking in quite a different
sense if you say, "But $x^2 - 1$ is zero if x is -1 or 1." We
went into this distinction in chapter 2.

The structure formed by the polynomials thus satisfies
all the field axioms except (*10*). If you will look back to
the chart in chapter 2, you will see that the integers did
exactly the same.

Question: Do the integers and the polynomials constitute isomorphic structures?

Division

In a field, division can be carried through without
remainder. In the structures we are now considering,
that cannot be done owing to the absence of axiom (*10*).
We can however carry out division in an amended sense.

44 divided by 9 gives 4 with remainder 8.
x^2 divided by $x - 1$ gives $x + 1$ with remainder 1.

How shall we describe what we do when we divide 44
by 9? We might say that we consider the multiples of 9,
and see which of them comes nearest to 44. This suggests
that 45 does, and that we might say 44 divided by 9 gives
5 with remainder -1. This might indeed give a simpler
and neater theory of division. We will, for the moment,
keep both possibilities in mind. The multiples of 9 are
the numbers $9n$. How near $9n$ is to 44 is estimated by
considering $44 - 9n$. We might make a table.

n	$44 - 9n$
2	26
3	17
4	8
5	−1
6	−10
7	−19

As we go away from $n = 4$ and $n = 5$, the numbers in the second column get numerically larger. $+8$ and $−1$, we may say, are the simplest numbers in the second column. It is a matter of opinion whether $+8$ or $−1$ is the simpler. In grade school arithmetic, 8 is definitely simpler, because it would take us so long to explain what we meant by $−1$. To someone familiar with the integers, however, $−1$ might well seem simpler than $+8$, since $|−1|$ is smaller than $|8|$.

Whichever view we adopt, we can say that the quotient is that number for which $44 - 9n$ is simplest. The remainder is the corresponding value of $44 - 9n$.

By either convention, the remainder is always simpler than the divisor. By the grade school convention, the remainder 8 is a simpler number than the divisor 9. By the other convention, since $|−1| < |9|$, $−1$ is simpler than 9.

This kind of division, then, implies that we have some way of deciding whether one element is simpler than another.

We know from experience that we can do long division with polynomials until we reach a remainder of *lower degree* than the divisor. Accordingly, we are led to make the convention that a polynomial $f(x)$ is simpler than a polynomial $g(x)$ if $f(x)$ is of lower degree than $g(x)$. We might expect to go further, and explain how we compare polynomials of equal degree, but for division this is not necessary. If polynomial $P(x)$ is to be divided by $D(x)$, there is only one $Q(x)$ that makes $P(x) - Q(x)D(x)$ of the lowest possible degree. This $Q(x)$ is called the quotient, and $P(x) - Q(x)D(x)$ is then the remainder $R(x)$.

For example, $x^2 - Q(x)(x - 1)$ is a constant only if $Q(x) = x + 1$. The remainder $R(x)$ is

$$x^2 - (x + 1)\ (x - 1), \quad \text{that is, } 1.$$

$R(x)$, of course, is not always a constant. For instance, when $x^3 + 2$ is divided by $x^2 - 1$, $Q(x) = x$ makes $(x^3 + 2) - Q(x)(x^2 - 1)$ the linear polynomial $x + 2$, and no other choice of $Q(x)$ will lead to any simpler result. Thus $R(x) = x + 2$.

The ordinary process of long division is equivalent to a series of steps in each of which the highest power of x is removed. Thus, when dividing $x^4 + x^3 + x^2 + x + 1$ by $x - 1$, we first subtract from $x^4 + x^3 + x^2 + x + 1$ the quantity $(x - 1)x^3$, which leaves $2x^3 + x^2 + x + 1$. From this we subtract $(x - 1)2x^2$ and obtain the quadratic $3x^2 + x + 1$. From this we subtract $(x - 1)3x$ and obtain $4x + 1$. Finally we subtract $(x - 1)4$, which leaves 5. All these steps can be combined in the statement

$$(x^4 + x^3 + x^2 + x + 1) - (x - 1)x^3 - (x - 1)2x^2$$
$$- (x - 1)3x - (x - 1)4 = 5.$$

In virtue of the distributive law (V'), this means that

$$(x^4 + x^3 + x^2 + x + 1)$$
$$- (x - 1)(x^3 + 2x^2 + 3x + 4) = 5.$$

Question: Give an interpretation of the steps in the usual arithmetical process of long division, when 12,345 is divided by 38.

Factors

With integers or polynomials, division usually leaves a remainder. It may however happen, as when 12 is divided by 3, or $x^2 - 1$ by $x - 1$, that the remainder is zero. In this case we say that the divisor is a factor. 3 is a factor of 12, $x - 1$ is a factor of $x^2 - 1$. d is a factor of p when, for some integer q, $qd = p$. $D(x)$ is a factor of $P(x)$ when, for some polynomial $Q(x)$, $Q(x)D(x) = P(x)$.

The numbers 1 and -1 are factors of every integer. For any integer n, $n = 1 \cdot n = (-1) \cdot (-n)$. This factorization is trivial.

DEFINITION.   *An element that is a factor of every element of a structure is called a unit.*

What are the units in the system of polynomials? We can eliminate at once any polynomial of the first or higher degree. For such a polynomial, $P(x)$, is certainly not a factor of $P(x) + 1$. There remain only the constant polynomials. Apart from zero, these are factors of every polynomial. For instance, 2 is a factor of $x + 1$ since $x + 1 = 2(\frac{1}{2}x + \frac{1}{2})$. You will remember that at the outset of this chapter we said we should accept as eligible any polynomial with *rational* coefficients.

Since any constant non-zero k is a factor of any polynomial, we also regard these factors as trivial. A teacher, wishing a class to see that $x^6 - 1$ could be factored as the difference of squares or as the difference of cubes, might ask, "Is there any way of starting to factor $x^6 - 1$ other than $(x^3 - 1)(x^3 + 1)$?" A pupil might suggest $(2x^3 - 2)(\frac{1}{2}x^3 + \frac{1}{2})$, and the teacher might say, "Well, that is really the same factorization, isn't it?" "Really the same" means that only a trivial operation has been performed.

In the same way, a pupil who factors $x^2 - 1$ as

$(2x - 2)(\frac{1}{2}x + \frac{1}{2})$ has undoubtedly given a correct answer. One might point out that $(x - 1)(x + 1)$ is a
somewhat more convenient form of this answer.

A *prime* element is one that has no factors except trivial
ones. Thus the factorization $(-1) \cdot (-3)$ does not prevent 3 from being a prime number. The factorization
$2(\frac{1}{2}x + \frac{1}{2})$ does not prevent $x + 1$ from being a prime
polynomial.

Note that we call an element prime when it has
no factors *within the structure*. For example, $3 =
(\sqrt{7} - 2)(\sqrt{7} + 2)$ and $x^2 - 2 = (x - \sqrt{2})(x + \sqrt{2})$.
But $\sqrt{7} - 2$ and $\sqrt{7} + 2$ are not integers, and $x - \sqrt{2}$
and $x + \sqrt{2}$ are not polynomials with rational coefficients. 3 and $x^2 - 2$ are prime elements of the integers
and of polynomials over rationals respectively.

Highest Common Factor

d is a common factor of a and b if $a = pd$, $b = qd$,
with p and q elements of the structure.

We now have to explain what we mean by the
"highest" common factor. We are looking, of course,
for an explanation that will hold, not only for the integers, but for any structure reasonably like the integers.

In chapter 3 we met a procedure for determining the
H.C.F. of two given integers a, b. These integers were
then thought of as being positive, but since the H.C.F.
of 8 and 12 is the same as the H.C.F. of 8 and -12,
this is no real restriction. This procedure led us to a
number h with the following properties:

(i) h is a common factor of a and b.

(ii) $h = au + bv$ for some u, v belonging to the
structure.

(iii) any common factor of a and b is a factor of h.

In property (ii) we say "belonging to the structure"

nstead of "which are integers" so that we shall not have o reword the statements when we proceed to consider tructures other than the integers.

It is evident that property (iii) is a direct consequence of property (ii). Property (iii) is stated here because it inks on to our experiences in elementary arithmetic, vhich statement (ii) does not.

We shall consider only structures in which a procedure analogous to the H.C.F. calculation of chapter 3 can be carried through. We suppose this structure to satisfy the field axioms, with the exception of (10). The proof in chapter 3 that h has properties (i)–(iii) depends only on these axioms.

Question: Check this last statement.

Any element h having properties (i)–(iii) will be called a H.C.F. Later we shall discuss what is involved in speaking of *the* H.C.F.

The H.C.F. process depended on repeated divisions. The field axioms, with (10) removed, are insufficient to guarantee division. As we saw in our analysis of division, ve need (1) a definition of "u is simpler than v", (2) the property that, given any elements a, b, it is possible to find an element q such that $r = a - qb$ is simpler than b.

We suppose our structure has a definition (1) and satisfies requirement (2). This is still not quite enough. The H.C.F. process of chapter 3, in the example there considered, gave the sequence of numbers 689, 481, 208, 65, 13, 0. These numbers get steadily smaller "simpler"). This is no accident. For instance, 65 arises as remainder for a division by 208. So it is bound to be impler than 208. The same holds for the other numbers n the sequence. The H.C.F., 13, is the number that occurs immediately before zero. Thus, an essential feature of the process is that it *must terminate*. Otherwise, there is no sense in speaking of the element just before the end.

We therefore require of our structure (3) that every sequence of elements, u_1, u_2, u_3, $\cdots$, for which u_{r+1} is simpler than u_r, terminates. It is impossible to have an unending sequence of elements, each simpler than its predecessor.

Here, of course, it is understood that the sequence has a first term u_1. For the integers one could have an infinite sequence, $\cdots$, 5, 4, 3, 2, 1, 0, without a beginning. The H.C.F. process automatically provides initial elements a, b. The sequence is bound to have a beginning. We demand that it shall also have an end.

In any structure, then, satisfying the field axioms with the exception of (10), and requirements (1) through (3) just listed, we can carry through the H.C.F. process, and find an element h with properties (i) through (iii).

In particular, the H.C.F. procedure can be carried out for polynomials over the rationals. We verify requirements (1), (2), (3), as follows.

A polynomial corresponds to a sequence $(a, b, c, \cdots , k, 0, 0, 0, \cdots)$. The complexity of a polynomial is measured by the number of terms that precede the unbroken run of zeros.

Thus a quadratic $(a, b, c, 0, 0, 0, \cdots)$ where $c \neq 0$ is less simple than a linear polynomial $(d, e, 0, 0, 0, \cdots)$ where $e \neq 0$, and this in turn is less simple than $(f, 0, 0, 0, \cdots)$ where $f \neq 0$, and this is less simple than $(0, 0, 0, 0, 0, \cdots)$, the polynomial zero. No polynomial simpler than zero can be found.

If $B(x)$ is any polynomial other than zero, the division process gives us $R(x)$, of the form $A(x) - Q(x)B(x)$, and this $R(x)$ is simpler than $B(x)$.

Finally, if $V_1(x)$ is any given polynomial, we cannot find an unending sequence $V_1(x)$, $V_2(x)$, $V_3(x)$, $\cdots$, with every $V_n(x)$ simpler than $V_{n-1}(x)$. For example, if $V_1(x)$ had 100 terms before the zeros, $V_2(x)$, being simpler than $V_1(x)$, could have at most 99. $V_3(x)$ could have at most 98. (Note that $V_n(x)$ is required to be *simpler than* $V_{n-1}(x)$. Its complexity must be *less*. "Less than or equal to" is not good enough.) So continuing, we see that $V_n(x)$ has at most $(101 - n)$ non-zero terms, until we reach $V_{100}(x)$ which has one non-zero term, and $V_{101}(x)$ which is zero. At this point, the sequence must terminate.

Requirements (1), (2), and (3) are thus met, and we can find the H.C.F. of two polynomials by a procedure closely akin to that for two integers.

In the example below, we find the H.C.F. of $x^4 - x^3 - 2x^2 + 2x - 4$ and $x^5 - 2x^3 - 3x^2 + x - 6$. It so happens that the stages of this process run exactly parallel to our earlier calculation, step for step, so that comparison is particularly easy.

$$
\begin{array}{r|r|r}
x + 2 & \begin{array}{l} x^4 - x^3 - 2x^2 + 2x - 4 \\ x^4 - x^3 - 3x^2 + 4x - 4 \end{array} & \begin{array}{l} x^5 - 2x^3 - 3x^2 + x - 6 \\ x^5 - 3x^3 \qquad\quad - 2x - 4 \end{array} \\ & \hline & \hline \\ & \begin{array}{l} x^2 - 2x \\ x^2 - 2x \end{array} & \begin{array}{l} x^3 - 3x^2 + 3x - 2 \\ x^3 - 3x^2 + 2x \end{array} \\ & \hline & \hline \\ & 0 & x - 2 \end{array}
$$

with the quotients $x + 1$ and $x - 1$ on the right.

The above example is very simple arithmetically, only integers being involved as coefficients. But it is not always possible to work without fractions appearing, as the next example shows. It was for this reason that we considered in this section polynomials with rational coefficients rather than polynomials with integral coefficients.

$$
\begin{array}{r|r|r}
-\tfrac{1}{3}x + \tfrac{2}{3} & \begin{array}{l} x^3 + 4x^2 + 4x + 3 \\ x^3 + 4x^2 - 3x - 18 \end{array} & \begin{array}{l} 2x^3 + 5x^2 - 10x - 21 \\ 2x^3 + 8x^2 + 8x + 6 \end{array} & 2 \\ & \hline & \hline \\ & 7x + 21 & \begin{array}{l} -3x^2 - 18x - 27 \\ -3x^2 - 15x - 27 \end{array} & -\tfrac{3}{7}x - \tfrac{9}{7} \\ & & \hline \\ & & 0 \end{array}
$$

This calculation gives the H.C.F. as $7x + 21$. As thi is $7(x + 3)$, we may remove the "unit" 7, and take $x +$ as a correct answer. In fact,

$$x^3 + 4x^2 + 4x + 3 = (x + 3)(x^2 + x + 1),$$
$$2x^3 + 5x^2 - 10x - 21 = (x + 3)(2x^2 - x - 7).$$

We have now shown an analogy between integers and polynomials in regard to division, factors, primes, units H.C.F. For we have explained all of these things in general terms that apply equally well to the two structure and, no doubt, to other structures also.

There remains one last point to clear up. How man elements h can satisfy the conditions?

(i) h is a common factor of a and b.

(ii) $h = au + bv$ for some u, v of the structure.

(iii) Any common factor of a, b is a factor of h.

Suppose that h and k both satisfy these. Then, in virtu of (i), k is a common factor of a and b. By (iii), k must b a factor of h. $\therefore h = ek$ for some e. Similarly, by inter changing the roles of h and k, $k = fh$ for some f. Henc $h = ek = efh$. Therefore $h(1 - ef) = 0$. h is not zero, so by axiom (12), $1 - ef = 0$. Hence $ef = 1$. If m is any element of the structure, $efm = m$. That is, e and f are factors of every element of the structure. Accordingly, and f are units.

For the integers this means that for $a = 12$, $b = 18$ the conditions (i) through (iii) are satisfied by 6 and $-$ and by no other numbers.

For the polynomials, if $A(x) = (x - 1)(x + 1)$ and $B(x) = (x - 1)(x + 2)$, then the conditions for $H(x$ are satisfied by $C(x - 1)$ for any constant C, and by n other polynomials.

This degree of uncertainty causes us no trouble. W have already seen that multiplication by a unit is a trivial change. If we know that numbers a and b both divide by 6, then we know that they both divide by -6. t is quite easy to show that if h satisfies properties (i)–(iii), so does hf, where f is a unit. This degree of vagueness n the answer is therefore unavoidable. And we proved that this is all the vagueness there is. We did this when ve showed that any k satisfying properties (i)–(iii) must be of the form hf.

We can, if we like, make a convention to fix h. For numbers we can say that h must be positive; we choose 6, rather than -6, for the H.C.F. of ± 12 and ± 18. For polynomials, we can require the coefficient of the highest power of x to be 1.

We shall exploit the analogy between integers and polynomials in the next chapter.

Chapter 5

An Application of the Analogy

WE HAVE MET two procedures for obtaining a new structure from an old one.

First, given any field F, we have shown how to construct polynomials over that field. That is, given a field F we show that it is always permissible to introduce a new symbol x and to assume that polynomials $a + bx + cx^2 + \cdots + kx^n$, where $a, b, c, \cdots, k$ are elements of F satisfy the commutative, associative, and distributive laws.

Second, given a structure such as the integers, we obtain a field from it in the following way. We select a prime element, p, of the structure, and we break the structure up into classes. Two elements belong to the same class if they leave the same remainder on division by p. If element a belongs to class A and element b to class B then $A + B$ means the class containing $a + b$, and AB the class containing ab. By a structure "such as the integers," we understand one in which all the field axioms except (10) apply, and also the three conditions listed in chapter 4 that make the H.C.F. process possible. We then know that the classes $A, B, \cdots$, form a field, for our proofs in chapters 3 and 4 used only the field axioms and the three conditions.

Both procedures we have a right to carry out. We do not need to have any doubts whether what we are doing is justified. We spent a good deal of time in chapter 2 showing that a new symbol x could always be brought in: it expressed merely the properties of sequences $a, b, c, \cdots, k, 0, 0, 0, \cdots$) formed from the elements of the field F. That is, it expressed the properties of something already there: it did not really bring in anything new. In the same way, the second procedure dealt with classes of elements in the structure. It, too, involved no new assumption.

It will be convenient to have names for these procedures, so that we can refer to them without a long explanation. The first procedure we will call *adjoining an indeterminate x to the field F*. In the second procedure, from a suitable structure S, we form *the residue classes modulo p*. Thus, the arithmetic of Even and Odd is the structure formed from the integers by considering the residue classes modulo 2. "Residue" is a word more or less synonymous with "remainder"; for some reason, it has become customary to use it in this connection.

Having these two procedures, we naturally look for structures to apply them to: in this way, we hope for a good crop of new structures.

The first procedure we have already applied to quite a number of fields: we have considered polynomials with real coefficients, polynomials with rational coefficients, polynomials with coefficients O, I, II, III, IV from the arithmetic modulo 5, and polynomials with coefficients from the other modular arithmetics. It is also possible to adjoin an indeterminate x to a structure that is not a field, as when we consider polynomials with integers as coefficients: the integers do not form a field. This however we have not investigated yet.

It does not look as though the first process is likely to

open new horizons for us. We have already used it quite
often; it has not led to any particularly novel idea.

How about the second process? So far, we have applied
it to one structure only—the integers, from which we
have obtained finite fields: the arithmetic of Even and
Odd, the arithmetics modulo 3, modulo 5, modulo 7,
and so on. To what else can we apply it? There is an
obvious candidate. In chapter 4 we saw that polynomials
resembled the integers very closely. The natural structure
to consider is that of polynomials. This still leaves us
some choice; we might consider polynomials with real
coefficients, or rational coefficients, or coefficients from
one of the modular arithmetics.

Suppose we pick polynomials with real coefficients.
When we obtained the arithmetic modulo 5 from the
integers, our first step was to choose the prime number 5.
Here, our first step must be to choose a prime polynomial—one that cannot be factored. $x^2 + 1$ is such a
polynomial. For suppose it had a factor. This factor
would have to be linear, say $bx - c$. Taking out the constant factor b, we can reduce $bx - c$ to the form $x - a$.
By the remainder theorem, $x - a$ is a factor of a polynomial $f(x)$ if and only if $f(a) = 0$. So $x - a$ is a factor
of $x^2 + 1$ only if $a^2 + 1$ is zero. But, for any real number
a, $a^2 + 1$ is larger than 1, hence not zero. So $x^2 + 1$ has
no factors within the set of polynomials with real coefficients. It is a prime polynomial. (In books on algebra
the word "irreducible" is usually employed instead of
"prime." The meaning is the same.)

Accordingly, if we begin with polynomials over the
real numbers and form the residue classes modulo
$(x^2 + 1)$, we are bound to arrive at a field.

When we constructed the arithmetic modulo 5, we
only needed the symbols O, I, II, III, IV because division by 5 could only give the remainders 0, 1, 2, 3,

Division by $x^2 + 1$ will never give as a remainder anything more complicated than a linear polynomial, $ax + b$. These remainders serve to label the various classes; one class consists of all the polynomials that leave remainder $x - 1$, and so on. A remainder may of course be constant. Thus $4x^2 + 6$ leaves remainder 2.

We introduce the following notation.

Let **1** stand for the class of polynomials that leave remainder 1.
Let **2** stand for the class of polynomials that leave remainder 2.
Let **3** stand for the class of polynomials that leave remainder 3.
Let **k** stand for the class of polynomials that leave remainder k.
Let **J** stand for the class of polynomials that leave remainder x.

This notation will prove sufficient for our needs.

Since x belongs to the class **J,** and 3 belongs to the class **3,** 3**J** is the class containing $3x$.

Since $3x$ belongs to the class **3J,** and 2 belongs to the class **2,** 3**J** + **2** is the class containing $3x + 2$.

In the same way, quite generally, **aJ** + **b** is the class containing $ax + b$.

We could now, if we liked, work out sums and products directly from the definition.

For example, to find $(2\mathbf{J} + 3)(4\mathbf{J} + 5)$, we could reason that $2\mathbf{J} + 3$ is the class containing $2x + 3$, and $4\mathbf{J} + 5$ is the class containing $4x + 5$. So $(2\mathbf{J} + 3)(4\mathbf{J} + 5)$ is the class containing $(2x + 3)(4x + 5)$. $(2x + 3)(4x + 5) = 8x^2 + 22x + 15$, which, on division by $x^2 + 1$, leaves $22x + 7$. The class containing $22x + 7$ is $22\mathbf{J} + 7$. Hence

$$(2\mathbf{J} + 3)(4\mathbf{J} + 5) = 22\mathbf{J} + 7.$$

But it is not really necessary to go through all this. For we know that the residue classes constitute a field. Accordingly, they obey the ordinary laws of algebra. So we may multiply out

$$(2\mathbf{J} + 3)(4\mathbf{J} + 5) = 8\mathbf{J}^2 + 22\mathbf{J} + 15.$$

Two points arise here. First, are we entitled to as-

sume that $2 \cdot 4 = 8$? Is it correct to multiply the bold
face numbers just as if they were ordinary numbers.
Second what is J^2?

The first question asks us to justify what we have
already done. The second points to still unexplored
territory.

The first point is soon dealt with; it does require us
to go back to the definition, but as the result is a general
rule, we are saved the bother of appealing to the definition each time. **2** is the class containing 2, **4** is the class
containing 4. By definition $2 \cdot 4$ is the class containing
$2 \cdot 4$, which is 8. The class containing 8 is called **8**
So $2 \cdot 4 = 8$.

The argument here used applies equally well to addition; it does not in any way depend on the particular
choice of the numbers 2 and 4. We conclude that the
boldface numbers can be added and multiplied by the
ordinary processes of arithmetic. We do not have to
learn any new tables. In technical language, the elements **k** are isomorphic to the numbers k.

We now come to the second point: what is J^2? Here
again, we go back to the definition of multiplication for
residue classes. **J** is the class to which x belongs, so $J \cdot$
is the class to which $x \cdot x$ belongs. That is, J^2 is the class
containing x^2. But when x^2 is divided by $x^2 + 1$ the
remainder is -1. Hence $J^2 = -1$.

We thus reach a striking conclusion. The element
$aJ + b$ can be added and multiplied by the ordinary
rules of arithmetic and algebra together with the equation

$$J^2 = -1.$$

We have, in effect, arrived at a theory of complex
numbers. **J** does what we expect the square root of
minus one to do.

Let us look back at what we have done. We began

with the field of real numbers. We applied two procedures to it, that we knew were permissible and would lead to a field. We obtained a field, containing elements **a**, that behaved exactly like the original real numbers a, and also containing an element **J** for which $\mathbf{J}^2 = -1$.

Since the elements **a** have exactly the same pattern as the numbers a, no harm will be done if we now forget the distinction between **a** and a. We can then say simply that to the real numbers a we adjoin a new element **J** for which $\mathbf{J}^2 = -1$. The structure so obtained is a field: that is to say, our algebraic habits do not have to be changed when we are working with it.

If you feel that there is something unfair in identifying **a** with a, it is quite possible to maintain the distinction between a and **a** and yet get information about the real numbers. We shall illustrate this by deriving a particular identity, of some mathematical and historical interest.

First of all, $(\mathbf{a} + \mathbf{bJ})(\mathbf{a} - \mathbf{bJ}) = \mathbf{a}^2 - \mathbf{b}^2\mathbf{J}^2 = \mathbf{a}^2 + \mathbf{b}^2$. Similarly, $(\mathbf{c} + \mathbf{dJ})(\mathbf{c} - \mathbf{dJ}) = \mathbf{c}^2 + \mathbf{d}^2$. Accordingly,

$$
\begin{aligned}
(\mathbf{a}^2 + \mathbf{b}^2)&(\mathbf{c}^2 + \mathbf{d}^2) \\
&= (\mathbf{a} + \mathbf{bJ})(\mathbf{a} - \mathbf{bJ})(\mathbf{c} + \mathbf{dJ})(\mathbf{c} - \mathbf{dJ}) \\
&= (\mathbf{a} + \mathbf{bJ})(\mathbf{c} - \mathbf{dJ})(\mathbf{a} - \mathbf{bJ})(\mathbf{c} + \mathbf{dJ}) \\
&= \{\mathbf{ac} + \mathbf{bd} + \mathbf{J}(\mathbf{bc} - \mathbf{ad})\}\{\mathbf{ac} + \mathbf{bd} - \mathbf{J}(\mathbf{bc} - \mathbf{ad})\} \\
&= (\mathbf{ac} + \mathbf{bd})^2 - \mathbf{J}^2(\mathbf{bc} - \mathbf{ad})^2 \\
&= (\mathbf{ac} + \mathbf{bd})^2 + (\mathbf{bc} - \mathbf{ad})^2.
\end{aligned}
$$

But we showed earlier that the elements **a, b, c, d** combined with each other in exactly the same way as the numbers a, b, c, d. In view of this isomorphism, we deduce that, for any real numbers a, b, c, d,

$$(a^2 + b^2)(c^2 + d^2) = (ac + bd)^2 + (bc - ad)^2.$$

This result is of some interest in the theory of numbers. Any whole number can be expressed as the sum of four squares. Thus, $7 = 4 + 1 + 1 + 1 = 2^2 + 1^2 + 1^2 + 1^2$.

We can easily see that 7 cannot be expressed as the sum of fewer than four squares; 1 and 4 are the only squares small enough to be used. It is thus a definite property of a whole number if it can be obtained by adding less than four squares together. For example, 13 is $9 + 4$, the sum of two squares. 17, being $16 + 1$, is also the sum of two squares. The identity above tells us that, when two such numbers are multiplied together, their product also is the sum of two squares. 13×17 is 221. If we put $a = 2, b = 3, c = 4, d = 1$ in the identity we get

$$13 \cdot 17 = 11^2 + 10^2,$$

and this expresses 221 as the sum of two squares.

The identity also has some relation to trigonometry.

This identity could, of course, be proved by means of elementary algebra without bringing **J** in at all. This must be so, for otherwise we should have got a result by using **J** that was not true for the algebra without **J**. But the whole point of our earlier work was to show that the presence of **J** did not make any logical difference: given the possibility of the algebra without **J,** the possibility of the algebra with **J** was a logical consequence.

Thus the introduction of **J** cannot lead to any extra results. We do not want it to; extra results would be wrong results. It can, however, lead to more convenient ways of obtaining known results. It can simplify proofs and illuminate theories. If you are sufficiently familiar with complex numbers, the proof of the identity given above is a natural one. It follows a train of thought that could lead you to the identity if you did not already know it. *

In trigonometry it is well known that many results can be obtained far more quickly and easily by using

* If $w = a + bJ, z = c - dJ$, the identity, in modulus notation, states $|w| \cdot |z| = |wz|$.

$\sqrt{-1}$ than by any other method. As the trigonometrical functions belong to analysis rather than to algebra (they require infinite processes for their definition), we shall not discuss them here. They are mentioned only as showing that the right to introduce $\sqrt{-1}$ is a valuable one.

For the present, it will be sufficient to consider our demonstration of the algebraic identity above. Someone might say that this particular result could be proved just as easily by elementary algebra. We are not concerned with this criticism. $\sqrt{-1}$ has proved itself very fruitful in many branches of mathematics; its claim to *usefulness* is not based solely on this particular identity. We are defending not the usefulness but the *correctness* of our method. Our proof may not be the neatest proof; but is it a proof at all?

"No," says our critic, "of course it isn't. You have a symbol **J** and you write $\mathbf{J}^2 = -1$. Well, that just is not so. You can't find a number **J** such that $\mathbf{J}^2 = -1$."

The interesting thing about this argument is that everything, except the conclusion, is correct. We do have a symbol **J** and we do write $\mathbf{J}^2 = -1$. It is also true that no number has its square equal to -1.

Our critic's mistake is in supposing that these true statements in any way detract from our proof of the identity. They do not. *We have at no point said that* **J** *represented a number.* All we assumed, in the various steps we took, was *that* **J** *obeyed the ordinary laws of algebra.* Our critic's assumption (probably based on something his teacher told him, authoritatively, and without any evidence to back it up) is that algebraic symbols always represent numbers.

It may help to summarize the rather lengthy process we have been through, if we present our argument in the form of a discussion with the critic.

Ourselves. I understand that you feel quite happy with calculations that only use real numbers, such as 2, -3, 3/4, $\sqrt{2}$, π?

Critic. Yes.

Ourselves. And you are then quite happy with polynomials such as $2x - 3$ or $x^2 + 2$, and you are able to calculate with these?

Critic. Yes.

Ourselves. In particular, you admit that it is possible to divide such polynomials by $x^2 + 1$ and see what remainder results.

Critic. Yes, of course.

Ourselves. So that, for instance, $x^3 + x + 2$ and $3x^2 + 5$, on division by $x^2 + 1$, both leave the remainder 2?

Critic. That is correct.

Ourselves. And there would be nothing vicious then in saying that all polynomials with this property could have the label **2** attached to them?

Critic. No. I cannot object to that.

Ourselves. And we could attach the label **J** to any polynomial that left remainder x, and the label -1 to any polynomial that left remainder -1?

Critic. Certainly.

Ourselves. Would there be any objection to recording in the form $2 \cdot \mathbf{x} = (2\mathbf{x})$ the fact that when any polynomial labeled **2** is multiplied by any polynomial labeled **x** the product is always to be labeled **2x**?

Critic. No. That is simply a notation, and does not commit me to any new admission.

Ourselves. And, similarly, we could explain the notation $2 + \mathbf{x}$?

Critic. Yes.

Ourselves. And we could then check that all the labels $\mathbf{aJ} + \mathbf{b}$, together with the signs $+$ and $\cdot$, obeyed the axioms (*1*) through (*12*) for a field?

Critic. I am willing to accept your word that anyone who did not find it too boring could do so.

Ourselves. And by means of these axioms we could justify all the steps taken with the symbols **a, b, c, d, J** in our demonstration of the identity?

Critic (after some thought). Yes; you have only handled these symbols in accordance with the rules allowed by axioms (1) through (12).

Ourselves. And finally we arrived at a result,

$$(\mathbf{a}^2 + \mathbf{b}^2)(\mathbf{c}^2 + \mathbf{d}^2) = (\mathbf{ac} + \mathbf{bd})^2 + (\mathbf{bc} - \mathbf{ad})^2,$$

in which **J** does not appear?

Critic. Yes.

Ourselves. But we also noticed that there was a very close resemblance between operations on the classes **a, b, c, d** and calculations with the corresponding numbers, a, b, c, d. For instance, can you find any example where $\mathbf{a} + \mathbf{b} = \mathbf{p}$ but $a + b$ is not p? Or one where $\mathbf{a} \cdot \mathbf{b} = \mathbf{q}$ and $a \cdot b$ is not q?

Critic (after trying a few examples, and making some algebraic calculations). No, there are no such cases.

Ourselves. And also if $\mathbf{a} - \mathbf{b} = \mathbf{r}$, then it must be that $a - b = r$?

Critic. Yes, certainly.

Ourselves. Our algebraic identity is built up by a chain of additions, subtractions, and multiplications?

Critic. Yes.

Ourselves. So the corresponding identity must hold for a, b, c, d?

Critic. Yes, it seems so.

Ourselves. In that case, we have proved our identity with the help of the symbol **J**, which does not represent a number. And you have admitted the logic of our procedure.

Critic. I feel I am being cheated, but I cannot say just where.

The idea of $\sqrt{-1}$ is still new enough for us to feel that it is strange. But in past centuries, it felt equally strange when the number $\sqrt{2}$ had to be brought in to describe the ratio between the lengths of the diagonal and the side of a square. Before that time, only rational numbers, p/q, with p and q integers, had been considered.

It was proved by the ancient Greeks that there cannot be a rational number x for which $x^2 = 2$. For if there were, this number could be expressed as p/q where p and q have no common factor (since any common factor could be canceled). In particular, we may assume that p and q are not both even: if they were both even, we could keep on canceling 2 until an odd numerator or denominator appeared. We suppose all possible canceling has been done, and that $(p/q)^2 = 2$; that is, $p^2 = 2q^2$. The square of an odd number is odd. But p^2, being $2q^2$, is even. Hence p cannot be odd. So p must be even. Hence q must be odd, as all possible canceling has been done. But, as p is even, we can write $p = 2k$. Then $p^2 = 2q^2$ shows that $4k^2 = 2q^2$ or $q^2 = 2k^2$. But q is odd, so q^2 is odd. $2k^2$ is even.

We have arrived at the conclusion that an odd number equals an even one. This is a contradiction. So there must have been something wrong with the assumption made at the outset, that $x^2 = 2$ could have a rational solution. Since this assumption leads to an absurdity, it must be false.

So an ancient Greek, who thought of numbers as consisting only of rational numbers, $3\frac{1}{2}$, $\frac{3}{4}$, $5\frac{1}{8}$, and so on, could have said, "No number has square equal to 2," with just as much conviction as our critic who said, "No number has square -1."

Our procedure is equally suitable for convincing him. We begin with the field of rationals, which he admits.

(An ancient Greek would not have recognized negative numbers. We suppose this difficulty to have been overcome first.) We adjoin to this an indeterminate x, and thus obtain polynomials with rational coefficients. We then select the prime polynomial $x^2 - 2$. This is prime over the rationals, for if it had a factor $x - a$ with a rational, then $a^2 - 2$ would be zero, and there is no rational number for which this happens. So, when we classify polynomials with rational coefficients in accordance with their remainders on division by $x^2 - 2$ (in other words, when we form the residue classes modulo $x^2 - 2$), we obtain a field.

Once again, we introduce a notation.

1 is the label for any polynomial leaving remainder 1.
2 is the label for any polynomial leaving remainder 2.
K is the label for any polynomial leaving remainder x.

Then $\mathbf{K}^2$ or $\mathbf{K} \cdot \mathbf{K}$, is the label for the class containing x^2. But x^2, on division by $x^2 - 2$, leaves remainder 2. So the class $\mathbf{K}^2$ is the class **2**.

$$\mathbf{K}^2 = \mathbf{2}$$

As division by $x^2 - 2$ leaves a linear remainder $a + bx$, all our labels are of the type

$$\mathbf{a + bK}.$$

We can prove results for rational numbers with the help of **K,** just as we proved results for real numbers with the help of **J.** The steps of the following argument run exactly parallel to the steps used earlier to establish an identity about the sums of squares.

$$(\mathbf{a + bK})(\mathbf{a - bK}) = \mathbf{a}^2 - \mathbf{b}^2\mathbf{K}^2 = \mathbf{a}^2 - 2\mathbf{b}^2.$$

Similarly,

$$(\mathbf{c + dK})(\mathbf{c - dK}) = \mathbf{c}^2 - 2\mathbf{d}^2.$$

Accordingly,

$(a^2 - 2b^2)(c^2 - 2d^2)$
$$= (a + bK)(a - bK)(c + dK)(c - dK)$$
$$= (a + bK)(c - dK)(a - bK)(c + dK)$$
$$= \{ac - 2bd + K(bc - ad)\}$$
$$\{ac - 2bd - K(bc - ad)\}$$
$$= (ac - 2bd)^2 - K^2(bc - ad)^2$$
$$= (ac - 2bd)^2 - 2(bc - ad)^2.$$

As before, there is an isomorphism relating **a, b, c, d**, to a, b, c, d, and we have, for rational numbers a, b, c, d, the relationship

$$(a^2 - 2b^2)(c^2 - 2d^2) = (ac - 2bd)^2 - 2(bc - ad)^2.$$

Once the logical correctness of introducing **K** with $K^2 = 2$ has been admitted, we may use the sign $\sqrt{2}$ instead of **K**; and finally, in view of the isomorphism between the classes **a** and the numbers a, we may drop the boldface. We thus reach our usual notation $a + b\sqrt{2}$.

EXERCISES

1. Show that, over the arithmetic modulo 3, the polynomial $x^2 + 1$ is prime (irreducible). Can a theory of complex numbers be constructed for the arithmetic modulo 3? Investigate and discuss.

2. Show that $x^2 + 3$ is an irreducible (that is, nonfactorable) polynomial over the arithmetic modulo 5. Is $x^2 + 1$ irreducible over the arithmetic modulo 5? Is a field obtained by applying the usual rules of arithmetic and algebra (i) to the elements $a + b\sqrt{-1}$, (ii) to the elements $a + b\sqrt{-3}$? a, b stand for the elements 0, 1, 2, 3, 4 (or O, I, II, III, IV, if you like) of the arithmetic modulo 5.

3. In the arithmetic modulo 2 it is possible to write down all the factorable quadratics, by listing all the expressions

$(x + a)(x + b)$ and multiplying them out. Do this. Is there any irreducible quadratic $x^2 + px + q$ over this arithmetic? If so, how many such quadratics are there?

4. Consider the residue classes, modulo $x^2 + x + 1$, of polynomials over the arithmetic modulo 2. Let **0** label the polynomials giving remainder 0, **1** label the polynomials giving remainder 1, **M** label the polynomials giving remainder x. Fill in the spaces of the multiplication table below.

	0	1	M	M + 1
0				
1				
M				
M + 1				

5. In question 4, let "modulo $x^2 + x + 1$" be replaced by "modulo $x^2 + 1$," the question otherwise remaining unaltered. Answer this amended question: Do the residue classes, modulo $x^2 + 1$, of polynomials over the arithmetic modulo 2, form a field? If not, which axioms fail?

6. Do the elements **0, 1, M, M + 1** of question 4 form a field?

7. Consider the residue classes, modulo x^2, of polynomials over the real numbers. Let **Q** label the class of polynomials that leave remainder x, **K** the class that leave remainder k, for any constant k. Find the product $(2 + 3Q) \cdot (4 + 5Q)$. Do the elements $a + bQ$ form a field?

8. Show that the H.C.F. procedure applied to $a + bx$ and $x^2 + 1$ enables us to find a linear polynomial $f(x)$ and a constant k such that $1 = (a + bx)f(x) + (x^2 + 1)k$. Find the polynomial $f(x)$ and deduce the reciprocal of $a + bJ$ where $J^2 = -1$.

9. What field results from considering the residue classes modulo x of polynomials over the reals? If $f(x)$ and $g(x)$ are two polynomials belonging to the same residue class modulo x, what can be said about the graphs of $y = f(x)$ and $y = g(x)$?

10. Determine the equation whose roots are the elements **0, 1, M, M + 1** of question 4.

Must We Distinguish Between 1 *and* **1**?

This is a point that troubles some students. In the ordinary course of development, we begin with numbers 0, 1, 2, 3, $\cdots$, as used in counting, the natural numbers. We then meet fractions, which we think of as lying between the natural numbers; $1\frac{1}{3}$, $1\frac{1}{2}$, $1\frac{2}{3}$ and many others lie between 1 and 2.

Then perhaps we meet negative numbers, -1, $-1\frac{1}{3}$, $-1\frac{1}{2}$, $-1\frac{2}{3}$, -2, $\cdots$, which we may think of as lying to the left of zero.

With the Pythagorean Theorem we meet $\sqrt{2}$, which lies between $1\frac{2}{5}$ and $1\frac{5}{12}$; from the circle we meet π, which lies between 3 and $3\frac{1}{7}$. These are irrational numbers.

Rational and irrational numbers together make up the real numbers. Then we go beyond these to consider complex numbers, $x + y\sqrt{-1}$. If y happens to be zero, the complex number reduces to a real number. We think of $4 + 0\sqrt{-1}$ as being simply the real number 4.

Thus real numbers are thought of as being part of the complex numbers; rational numbers as part of real numbers; integers as part of rationals; the natural numbers as part of the integers. All this we think while in a state of innocence.

Then we meet a mathematical philosopher who points out that, in order to justify the use of $\sqrt{2}$, we had to bring in a symbol **K,** a label for any polynomial that left remainder x on division by $x^2 - 2$. **K** thus stood for a collection of polynomials. In the same way **2** stood for a collection of polynomials—all those that leave remainder 2 on division by $x^2 - 2$. Then we had $\mathbf{K}^2 = \mathbf{2}$. Now, says the philosopher, the number 2 is a very different thing from **2,** a collection of polynomials. Admittedly there is an isomorphism, $2 + 3 = 5$ corresponding to $2 + 3 = 5$. But 2 and **2** are different things, and you must not forget this.

Now this matter is somewhat crucial, for an argument of this kind arises at each step in the extension of number. In passing from whole numbers to fractions, a philosophical theory considers number pairs (p, q) which eventually turn out to play the role of p/q. Now a number pair is not the same thing as a number, so (says the philosopher) we must distinguish between the natural number 4 and the fraction $(4, 1)$ or $4/1$.

Negative numbers also can be introduced by number pairing. Thus $+4$ corresponds to any pair such as $(7, 3)$ in which the first number is 4 *more* than the second, -4 to any pair such as $(5, 9)$ in which the first number is 4 *less* than the second. Thus the philosopher distinguishes between the natural number 4 and the positive integer $+4$.

In the same way a distinction is drawn between the integer $+4$ and the real number 4, and between the real number 4 and the number $4 + 0\sqrt{-1}$ occurring in complex number theory.

Thus, according to this philosopher, the real numbers do not form part of the complex, nor the rationals of the reals, nor the integers of the rationals, nor the natural numbers of the integers.

How are we to decide what value to attach to such philosophical arguments? The correct procedure is, I think, indicated in a passage of a well-known children's book.

> The first person he met was Rabbit.
> "Hallo, Rabbit," he said, "is that you?"
> "Let's pretend it isn't," said Rabbit, "and see what happens."
>
> *Winnie-the-Pooh*

Rabbit here seems to be taking a thoroughly scientific position. Let us apply his approach to the point at issue. Suppose you cling to the viewpoint of innocence, that the natural numbers, the integers, the rationals, the reals, the complex numbers are like a set of boxes, each contained in the following one. To what errors will this supposition lead you? So far as I can see, it will not lead you to any.

Nor, on the other hand, do I see that the philosopher who insists that $+4$ is different from 4 is necessarily going to be led into any particular error. The whole question seems to be about ways of looking at things, rather than about any point of fact. We often have difficulty in saying whether or not two things are "the same." Is the man of seventy the same person as the boy who used to attend the village school? In one sense, yes; in another sense, no.

This difficulty is particularly acute when we are talking about abstract ideas, when we are trying to decide whether the natural number 4 is the same as the fraction $4/1$ or different.

Suppose you say, "The conductor stopped the band after it had played four bars." Which "four" are you using there? Since you can count the four bars, it would be reasonable to answer, "The natural number four, the four we use when we count 1, 2, 3, 4." But suppose the conductor had intervened a little later, when the band had played four and one-half bars. $4\frac{1}{2}$ is clearly a fraction, a rational number. This suggests that the 4 in "four bars" could be regarded as a rational number equally well. My own feeling is that it does not matter which you call it, that the distinction between natural number, positive integer, rational number, real number, cannot be maintained in such situations—in fact, that there is a lot to be said for the viewpoint of innocence. It would be most unconventional to say that the band played for $4 + 0\sqrt{-1}$ bars, but I do not know that anyone could say you were actually wrong if you did this. So far as I can see, it passes Rabbit's test: no disaster would overtake you if you did it.

What do we mean by saying that two mathematical systems are "the same"? Consider some examples. If you had two calculating machines that were identical except that the numbers on one were written in black, on the other in blue, would you say they represented the same system? Everyone, I imagine, would say "Yes." Next, suppose that the two machines gave the same results, but that their internal mechanisms were different—one perhaps using gear wheels, the other being electronic. Would you still say they embodied the same system? My own answer would be "Yes."

Now suppose we have two calculating machines. The first has keys marked in black, and it carries out addition and multiplication for the tables shown here. Call this the black system.

$+$	0	I	M	$M + I$
0	0	I	M	$M + I$
I	I	0	$M + I$	M
M	M	$M + I$	0	I
$M + I$	$M + I$	M	I	0

$\times$	0	I	M	$M + I$
0	0	0	0	0
I	0	I	M	$M + I$
M	0	M	$M + I$	I
$M + I$	0	$M + 1$	I	M

We also have the blue system, a machine with keys marked in blue, that performs operations for the tables shown here.

+	O	I
O	O	I
I	I	O

×	O	I
O	O	O
I	O	I

You will notice that the top left-hand corners of the "black" tables are the same as the "blue" tables. Shall we say then that the blue system is a part of the black system? If we accept the earlier contention, that differences of color and of internal mechanism are unimportant, we are bound to answer "Yes." The blue machine is not, of course, part of the black machine, but the mathematical system represented by, or embodied in, the blue machine is part of the mathematical system represented by the black machine.

Now the blue system is, of course, the arithmetic modulo 2, and the black system is the field obtained from that arithmetic (as in question 4, p. 107) by considering residue classes for the irreducible polynomial $x^2 + x + 1$.

Our philosopher arrived at these systems in that order. He first had the blue O and I standing for Even and Odd. Then he brought in the black O as a label for any polynomial over the arithmetic modulo 2 that happened to be exactly divisible by $x^2 + x + 1$ (which you can write $Ix^2 + Ix + I$, with blue I's, if you like). The black I, the black M, and the black $M + I$ were given similar meanings.

Having arrived at the black system in this way, our philosopher cannot get it out of his head that the black O has a different meaning from the blue O. He maintains that the blue system is *not* a part of the black system, because of this difference of meaning.

Now we are grateful to him for pointing out that the black system can be derived, built up, from the blue system. That is a most helpful observation, and we shall often make use of it. But because this is "a" way of doing things, it does not follow that it is "the" only way of doing things. In mathematics, it very often happens that a complicated structure is discovered before a simple one. The black system might have been discovered before the blue one. Then, we should have discussed it in its own right. We should have checked to see that it satisfied all the axioms for a field. We could do all this without mentioning the blue system, without even being aware that the blue system was possible at all. Then someone might have noticed that the northwest corners of the black tables already constituted a closed system, a field, with elements O and I. The blue system would then have been discovered, and thought of, as a part of the black system.

In the same way, we arrived at the complex numbers earlier in this chapter by considering the residue classes modulo $x^2 + 1$. This is one way of obtaining the complex numbers, but there are others. One can derive $p + q\sqrt{-1}$ by considering the number pair (p, q); in another treatment, $\sqrt{-1}$ is related to rotation through a right angle; in yet another, matrix theory is used. We do not regard these as different complex number systems, but rather as different ways of realizing one and the same pattern. It is a waste of time to argue whether $\sqrt{-1}$ "really is" a residue class of polynomials, or the number pair $(0, 1)$, or a rotation through $90°$, or a particular matrix.

I do not believe that any mathematical result at all comes from the discussion in the last few pages. I have included this discussion for two reasons. First, we naturally feel that something questionable is being done when we "identify" **1,** standing for a collection of polynomials, with the number 1. Second, students pick up wisps and echoes of the philosophical discussions, on whether the integer 4 and the rational number 4/1 are the same or different, and are bothered by these. Of one thing I am certain: it is a mistake to lose any sleep over such matters. The question is psychological rather than philosophical or scientific. You should feel perfectly free to adopt whichever answer allows you to work most happily: indeed, if it suits you, you can adopt now one view, now the other, according to the problem you are working on.

Chapter 6

Extending Fields

IN CHAPTER 5 we considered a way of extending a given
field. The method used the idea of residue classes, but,
as we saw in a lengthy discussion, it was often inconvenient to keep the final result in terms of residue classes.
The residue classes gave us a way of showing that a
certain type of calculating machine could be built, and
indeed of building it. However, once having obtained the
new machine, we shall often want simply to work it,
and to forget what is inside it. So let us look at the fields
we obtain by the procedure of chapter 5, and see just
what this procedure does for us.

At the beginning of chapter 5, by considering residue
classes modulo $(x^2 + 1)$, we obtained the symbols $a + bJ$
where a and b are real numbers and J satisfies the equation $J^2 = -1$. $a + bJ$ is commonly referred to as a
"complex number." In order to work correctly with
complex numbers, all you need to know is (i) that
complex numbers obey the laws of algebra, (ii) that
$J^2 = -1$. Statement (i) here could be put, that complex
numbers form a field. As the real numbers form a field,
in passing from real numbers to complex numbers, we
are not conscious of any change, so far as statement (i)
goes. The main novelty lies in statement (ii), that
$J^2 = -1$. So long as we are working with the real

numbers, the equation $x^2 + 1 = 0$ has no solution. The effect of passing to the complex numbers is to bring in a new symbol J, such that $J^2 + 1 = 0$. We thus, so to speak, create a root for the equation $x^2 + 1 = 0$. You will notice that the procedure of chapter 5 used residue classes modulo $(x^2 + 1)$.

In the same way, toward the end of chapter 5, to obtain a field in which $x^2 - 2 = 0$ had a root, we considered residue classes modulo $(x^2 - 2)$.

Quite generally, if $f(x)$ is an irreducible polynomial over a field F, we can obtain a field in which the equation $f(x) = 0$ has a root by considering residue classes modulo $f(x)$.

(You should be able to prove this result, by observing the proofs on pages 98 and 105, for $J^2 + 1 = 0$ and $K^2 - 2 = 0$, and noting that the method used in these two particular proofs can be used in general. A proof will be given shortly, but it does no more than carry out the hint here given: if you can find the proof unaided, you will gain in insight and confidence.)

In speaking above of statements (i) and (ii) as embodying all you need to know to calculate with complex numbers, I should perhaps have added something you need to know is *not* so. A student might write $2J - 3 = 0$, and say "Why not? How do you know this is not so?" In this particular case, it is easy enough to show that this equation is wrong. If $2J - 3 = 0$, $J = 1\frac{1}{2}$, so $J^2 = -1$ would mean $(1\frac{1}{2})^2 = -1$, which is not so.

However, with an eye on the general moral we are hoping to draw, we might state (ii) more fully; $J^2 = -1$ and J does not satisfy any simpler equation (that is, any equation of lower degree). We are now ready to state our general theorem.

THEOREM. *If F is any field, and $f(x)$ is an irreducible polynomial over F, we can always construct a new field, con-*

taining the elements of F and also a new symbol Q for which f(Q) = 0 but Q does not satisfy any equation of lower degree.

Residue classes are not mentioned at all in the statement of this theorem, but of course we go back to residue classes for our proof that the new field can be constructed. However, when we *apply* this theorem, we need not think of residue classes at all, unless we want to.

Proof. It will be convenient to write the proof out on the assumption that $f(x)$ is a cubic. It should be clear that the ideas of the proof work equally well for a polynomial of any degree.

If k is any constant, the equations $f(Q) = 0$ and $kf(Q) = 0$ are equivalent; $f(x)$ being irreducible and $kf(x)$ being irreducible are also equivalent. Thus we do not lose any generality if we suppose $f(x)$ to have the coefficient 1 for the highest power of x.

Suppose then that $f(x)$ is $x^3 - ax^2 - bx - c$. We consider residue classes of polynomials over F, modulo $f(x)$. Since $f(x)$ is irreducible, these residue classes will form a field.

Let **a** stand for the class containing a.
Let **b** stand for the class containing b.
Let **c** stand for the class containing c.
Let **Q** stand for the class containing x.

You will remember that addition and multiplication of classes were defined by means of representatives. For instance, in the arithmetic modulo 5, we found $III \cdot IV$ by taking 3, an element in class III, and multiplying it by 4, an element in class IV. $3 \cdot 4 = 12$, and 12 is in class II, so $III \cdot IV = II$. We showed (in chapter 3) that it did not matter which representatives we took. We might, for example, have chosen 8 to represent class III and 19 to represent IV. $8 \cdot 19 = 152$, and 152 is in class II, so we still reach the result $III \cdot IV = II$.

We are now working with polynomials, but (as chapter 4 stressed, and chapter 5 applied) polynomials can be handled much like integers. We thus find

$\mathbf{Q^3}$ is the class containing x^3.
$\mathbf{aQ^2}$ is the class containing ax^2.
$\mathbf{bQ}$ is the class containing bx.
$\mathbf{c}$ is the class containing c.

Combining these, we see that $\mathbf{Q^3} - \mathbf{aQ^2} - \mathbf{bQ} - \mathbf{c}$ is the class containing $x^3 - ax^2 - bx - c$. But $x^3 - ax^2 - bx - c$ is $f(x)$; on division by $f(x)$ it leaves remainder zero. Hence it belongs to the class $\mathbf{0}$. Therefore $\mathbf{Q^3} - \mathbf{aQ^2} - \mathbf{bQ} - \mathbf{c}$ and $\mathbf{0}$ are labels for the same class, that is

$$\mathbf{Q^3} - \mathbf{aQ^2} - \mathbf{bQ} - \mathbf{c} = \mathbf{0}.$$

We now have to finish off the argument, as we did in chapter 5, to show that we could drop the boldface and write

$$Q^3 - aQ^2 - bQ - c = 0,$$

that is,

$$f(Q) = 0.$$

This is the main result we wanted to show. But we also have the negative result to prove, that Q does not satisfy any equation of lower degree. This comes very simply from considering residue classes.

Suppose someone claimed that Q satisfied an equation $pQ^2 + rQ + s = 0$. I suppose here that p, r, s are not all zero. If someone says $0 \cdot Q^2 + 0 \cdot Q + 0 = 0$, we can only agree with him. That is perfectly correct, but it is trivial; if you like, you can reword the theorem to exclude this case specifically.

Suppose, then, it is claimed that $pQ^2 + rQ + s = 0$. In terms of residue classes, this means that $\mathbf{pQ^2} + \mathbf{rQ} + \mathbf{s} = \mathbf{0}$. $\mathbf{pQ^2} + \mathbf{rQ} + \mathbf{s}$ is the class containing $px^2 + rx + s$. The equation asserts that $px^2 + rx + s$ leaves remainder

0 on division by $x^3 - ax^2 - bx - c$. But this is so only if p, r, s are all zero, and we have already excluded this trivial case.

We have now proved all the assertions contained in the theorem. Q.E.D.

It will be convenient to make a remark about the new field while we still have in mind the symbols as defined in the proof of the theorem. We want to show that the facts given in the theorem completely replace the residue-class approach so far as making calculations is concerned.

With $f(x)$ cubic, it is clear, on the residue-class approach, that we never need anything higher than a quadratic in $\mathbf{Q}$ to write down an element of the new field. For the remainder, on dividing any polynomial by a cubic $f(x)$, will be at most a quadratic in x, and its label will be at most quadratic in $\mathbf{Q}$. How is this result arrived at with the new approach?

The theorem does give us a way of getting rid of all powers of Q above the second. For it states $f(Q) = 0$, and this is equivalent to

$$Q^3 = aQ^2 + bQ + c. \qquad (\text{I})$$

(It was in anticipation of this equation that $f(x)$ was defined as $x^3 - ax^2 - bx - c$, rather than with positive signs.)

Accordingly, we have a quadratic expression that can always be substituted for Q^3. If we multiply both sides of equation (I) by Q, we obtain

$$Q^4 = aQ^3 + bQ^2 + cQ. \qquad (\text{II})$$

Substitute in (II) the value of Q^3 given by (I). We find

$$Q^4 = a(aQ^2 + bQ + c) + bQ^2 + cQ$$
$$= (a^2 + b)Q^2 + (ab + c)Q + ac. \qquad (\text{III})$$

It is evident that by continuing in this way, any

power whatever of Q can be expressed as a quadratic in Q. Hence any polynomial in Q can be reduced to a quadratic.

Thus, if we take two quantities of the form $rQ^2 + sQ + t$ and add or multiply them, the result is always expressible in this form.

We can show, too, that every such quantity other than zero has a reciprocal of the same type. Let $g(Q) = rQ^2 + sQ + t$. By the H.C.F. procedure, applied to the polynomials $g(Q)$ and $f(Q)$, we can find polynomials $u(Q)$ and $v(Q)$ such that

$$g(Q)u(Q) + f(Q)v(Q) = 1.$$

But $f(Q) = 0$. Hence

$$g(Q)u(Q) = 1.$$

$u(Q)$ is a polynomial in Q. Actually, the H.C.F. process will yield a quadratic $u(Q)$ and a linear $v(Q)$. But we can save ourselves the trouble of proving this by means of the remark above, that any polynomial in Q can be reduced to a quadratic.

Thus $1/g(Q)$ can be expressed as a quadratic in Q.

Division by $g(Q)$ can be achieved by multiplying by $1/g(Q)$.

These considerations are intended to illustrate the fact that the properties of the new field can be obtained from the information contained in the theorem alone—that is, by purely algebraic calculations, without any mention of residue classes or the meaning of Q. We appeal to residue classes to satisfy our scientific conscience, to show that what we are doing is justified. But once the foundations have been laid, we can proceed purely by calculation—as, of course, mathematicians did for centuries with $\sqrt{-1}$ and $\sqrt{2}$ before the residue-class explanation was thought of.

The field formed by adjoining the element Q to the field F is often denoted by $F(Q)$. This, of course, has nothing to do with the symbol for *function*, such as $f(x)$.

For example, if R stands for the field of real numbers, $R(\sqrt{-1})$ will stand for the field obtained from R by introducing the new element $\sqrt{-1}$; that is, $R(\sqrt{-1})$ stands for the complex numbers.

Question: Verify by calculation that the elements $r\sqrt[3]{4} + s\sqrt[3]{2} + t$ (r, s, t rational numbers) can be added, subtracted, multiplied, and divided, the results always being expressible in the same form. (This is the particular case where $f(x) = x^3 - 2$, so $Q = \sqrt[3]{2}$, $Q^2 = \sqrt[3]{4}$.) Find, in this form, the reciprocal of

$$\sqrt[3]{4} + 2\sqrt[3]{2} + 3.$$

Two Finite Fields

As an illustration of these ideas, we shall consider two fields obtained as extensions of the arithmetic modulo 2. These fields contain only a finite number of elements so that they are very compact and easily surveyed.

The procedure, as explained earlier, is to select an irreducible polynomial $f(x)$, and then introduce a new symbol, say Q, such that $f(Q) = 0$.

We first choose an irreducible quadratic for $f(x)$; later we study what happens when an irreducible cubic is chosen. The irreducible quadratic has already been touched on in various examples (pp. 106–107, questions 3, 4, 6, 10). The discussion of the irreducible cubic is equally suitable for an example. After reading the account of the irreducible quadratic here, you may well wish to work out the other question for yourself, and see what properties you can observe or prove in the field you obtain.

A Field with Four Elements

We propose to join a new element, M, to the arithmetic modulo 2. M is to be the root of an irreducible quadratic. Our first step, then, must be to find an irreducible quadratic. We can easily list all the quadratics that are reducible. Any that do not appear on this list must necessarily be irreducible.

The only possible linear factors are x and $x + 1$, since 0, 1 are the only elements of the arithmetic. The factors of the quadratic may be both x; or both $x + 1$; or one of each.

Thus, the only quadratics that factor are

$$x \cdot x = x^2$$
$$x \cdot (x + 1) = x^2 + x$$
$$(x + 1) \cdot (x + 1) = x^2 + 1$$

Every quadratic is of the form $x^2 + px + q$, where p may be 0 or 1, and q also may be 0 or 1.

Thus, every possible quadratic appears in the scheme below.

	$p = 0$	$p = 1$
$q = 0$	x^2	$x^2 + x$
$q = 1$	$x^2 + 1$	$x^2 + x + 1$

Three of these quadratics have already been listed as reducible. One only remains, $x^2 + x + 1$, and this is irreducible. Accordingly, we introduce M to provide a root for this polynomial. That is, we assume

$$M^2 + M + 1 = 0.$$

Since we are working in the arithmetic modulo 2, this equation is equivalent to

$$M^2 = M + 1.$$

(Justification. Add M^2 to both sides of the earlier equation, and use $1 + 1 = 0$ for the coefficient of M^2 on the left-hand side. $M + 1 = M^2$ is the result.)

By means of this equation, we can always replace M^2 by $M + 1$, and thus we never need to have the square of M, or any higher power, left in an expression: we can always simplify until a polynomial is reduced to linear form.

Thus, all our elements will be expressible in the form $aM + b$, where a and b take the values 0, 1. So we have the scheme:

	$b = 0$	$b = 1$
$a = 1$	M	$M + 1$
$a = 0$	0	1

This shows that the new field contains only four elements 0, 1, M, $M + 1$.

The addition and multiplication tables for these four elements are:

	0	1	M	$M + 1$
0	0	1	M	$M + 1$
1	1	0	$M + 1$	M
M	M	$M + 1$	0	1
$M + 1$	$M + 1$	M	1	0

	0	1	M	$M + 1$
0	0	0	0	0
1	0	1	M	$M + 1$
M	0	M	$M + 1$	1
$M + 1$	0	$M + 1$	1	M

The addition table is easily obtained: we have only to remember, since we are working modulo 2, that $1 + 1$ and $M + M$ are both zero.

In the multiplication table, we need to use the equation $M^2 = M + 1$. Thus

$$M \cdot M = M^2 = M + 1$$
$$M \cdot (M + 1) = M^2 + M$$
$$= (M + 1) + M = 1$$
$$(M + 1) \cdot (M + 1) = M^2 + 2M + 1 = M^2 + 1$$
$$= (M + 1) + 1 = M.$$

The values thus found have been entered in the multiplication table above.

On seeing this multiplication table for the first time, students often comment on the pattern it displays—the stripes running from northeast to southwest. It is interesting to observe such a pattern. However, it is a mistake merely to notice a pattern, and pass on.

Very often a mathematical discovery starts with an observation of some pattern. Then one asks, "What is this pattern? Why does it occur here? How can it be made to yield a mathematical theorem or principle?" After thought and analysis, one can often reach a result much more definite and useful than the original recognition of a superficial pattern. The next few paragraphs follow the lines of an actual class discussion. All the answers are those produced by the students.

First of all, then, what is the pattern we have seen? If we leave out the border of zeros, the multiplication table has the following pattern.

a	b	c
b	c	a
c	a	b

Where have we seen this kind of pattern before? In the arithmetic modulo n. In which table did it occur? In the addition table: the addition tables always showed this northeast-to-southwest striped effect. All the addition tables had this general type of pattern: did any particular

table actually reproduce the identical pattern above?
Yes: the arithmetic modulo 3. (See your answers to
questions on page 15–16.)

Our result is now rather more definite: the *multiplication* table in our field reproduces the pattern of the
addition table modulo 3. This is in itself quite striking.
We have the following correspondence.

Field elements	Numbers modulo 3
1	0
M	1
$M + 1$	2

Multiplication in the first column corresponds to addition in the second column. What does that remind us of?
Logarithms. We could in fact use the table above exactly
like a table of logarithms, for example, to multiply M
by $M + 1$. Opposite M we find 1, opposite $M + 1$
we find 2. Add 1 to 2. The sum (modulo 3) is 0. Now we
decode ("take antilogarithms"). 0 stands opposite to 1.
So the answer is 1, which is correct.

What, then, is a logarithm? The usual definition is
that $\log_b a = x$ if $a = b^x$. A table of logarithms is just a
table of powers, read the other way round.

So our little table above suggests that there is some b
such that

$$1 = b^0,$$
$$M = b^1,$$
$$M + 1 = b^2.$$

The middle entry here tells us what the base b of our
log table is: $b = M$. In fact, then,

$$1 = M^0,$$
$$M = M^1,$$
$$M + 1 = M^2.$$

In our field, then, every element except zero is a power of M.

Why should modulo 3 come into it? Let us continue to calculate the powers of M:

$$M^3 = M \cdot M^2 = M(M + 1) = M^2 + M = 1,$$
$$M^4 = M \cdot M^3 = M,$$
$$M^5 = M \cdot M^4 = M^2,$$
$$M^6 = M \cdot M^5 = M^3 = 1.$$

It is pretty clear now that, for any whole number n,

$$M^{3n} = 1,$$
$$M^{3n+1} = M,$$
$$M^{3n+2} = M^2.$$

Accordingly, if you want to find any power of M, say M^k, where k is a whole number, all you need to know is whether k leaves remainder 0, 1, or 2 on division by 3. That is why modulo 3 comes into the picture.

A modular arithmetic always comes in when we are dealing with roots of unity. For example $(-1)^k$ is 1 if k is even, -1 if k is odd.

It is clear that sooner or later the powers of an element of the field must recur. Otherwise we could go on forever, forming M, M^2, M^3, M^4, $\cdots$, and getting new elements all the time. But the field contains only four elements; the supply of new elements must give out pretty quickly. This type of argument clearly applies to any field with a finite number of elements.

Our inquiry naturally raises a number of general questions. Can an irreducible polynomial $f(x)$ of any desired degree k be found for the arithmetic modulo n (n prime)?

If so, we can construct a field by adjoining an element M for which $f(M) = 0$ is assumed. Will all the elements of this field, apart from zero, be powers of M? Or is this property confined to the case we have just considered? Or does it hold sometimes but not always?

The answers to these questions are known and can be found in standard texts, such as Van der Waerden's *Modern Algebra*. You may derive some entertainment by collecting evidence bearing on these questions and trying to discover, or to prove, the answers for yourself. Some relevant evidence is provided later in this chapter, when we study a field with eight elements.

It may be worth noting a curious symmetry between the elements M and $M + 1$.

> M is a root of the equation $x^2 + x + 1 = 0$. So is $M + 1$.
> If you add 1 to M you get $M + 1$
> If you add 1 to $M + 1$ you get M.
> If you square M you get $M + 1$.
> If you square $M + 1$ you get M.
> Every element of the field, except 0 is a power of M.
> Every element of the field, except 0, is a power of $M + 1$.

This symmetry is significant and plays an important role in more advanced theory.

A Field with Eight Elements

We now begin to construct another field. We shall work much as we did on the field with four elements, except that we shall begin by seeking an irreducible cubic rather than an irreducible quadratic.

There are eight cubics, since in $x^3 + px^2 + qx + r$ each of p, q, r can be 0 or 1. As before, we begin by listing all those that *can* be factored. A cubic can factor into a linear factor and an irreducible quadratic, or it may break up completely into linear factors. The following list covers all the possibilities:

$$x(x^2 + x + 1) = x^3 + x^2 + x,$$
$$(x + 1)(x^2 + x + 1) = x^3 + 1,$$
$$x \cdot x \cdot x = x^3,$$
$$x \cdot x(x + 1) = x^3 + x^2,$$
$$x \cdot (x + 1)^2 = x^3 + x,$$
$$(x + 1)^3 = x^3 + x^2 + x + 1.$$

Two cubics remain. They are $x^3 + x + 1$ and $x^3 + x^2 + 1$. These are the irreducible cubics over the arithmetic modulo 2. We could choose either of them. Suppose we choose $x^3 + x + 1$.

Our next step is to introduce Q with the assumption $Q^3 + Q + 1 = 0$, which is the same thing as saying $Q^3 = Q + 1$.

This equation shows that we need never keep Q^3 or any higher power in any expression. All our elements can be put in the form $aQ^2 + bQ + c$. Earlier we arranged

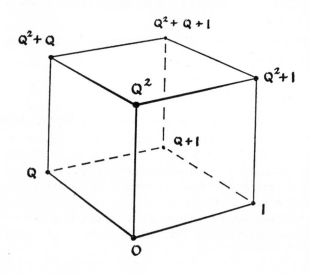

the four elements of the other field systematically in a square (on p. 123). To arrange our present eight elements systematically, we need a cube.

The floor of the cube corresponds to $a = 0$, the ceiling to $a = 1$; the front to $b = 0$, the back to $b = 1$; the left to $c = 0$, the right to $c = 1$.

In our earlier work, the powers of M gave us all the non-zero elements of the field. Do the powers of Q do the same now? To answer this, we calculate the powers of Q.

$$Q^0 = 1,$$
$$Q^1 = Q,$$
$$Q^2 = Q^2,$$
$$Q^3 = Q + 1, \text{ our basic assumption,}$$
$$Q^4 = Q \cdot Q^3 = Q^2 + Q,$$
$$Q^5 = Q \cdot Q^4 = Q^3 + Q^2 = Q^2 + Q + 1,$$
$$Q^6 = Q \cdot Q^5 = Q^3 + Q^2 + Q = Q^2 + 1,$$
$$Q^7 = Q \cdot Q^6 = Q^3 + Q = 1.$$

(The last step in finding Q^5, Q^6, and Q^7 consisted in substituting $Q + 1$ for Q^3, and simplifying, with the arithmetic modulo 2.)

Q^0 through Q^6 are all different; they give us seven elements of the field: zero is the eighth. Once again all the non-zero elements are powers of a single element

EXERCISES

1. What arithmetic modulo n plays the role for the field with eight elements that the addition modulo 3 played for the field with four elements?

2. Every non-zero element can be represented as a power of Q. Is Q the only element with this property? If not, what other elements have it?

3. The equation $x^3 + x + 1 = 0$ has the root Q. Has it any other roots in the field with eight elements?

4. The cubic $x^3 + x^2 + 1$ is irreducible over the arithmetic modulo 2. Is it irreducible over the field with eight elements? Do any elements of the field satisfy the equation $x^3 + x^2 + 1 = 0$?

5. If we had chosen $x^3 + x^2 + 1$ instead of $x^3 + x + 1$ for our irreducible $f(x)$, would it have made any essential difference to the work? Should we have arrived at the same field?

6. Which powers of Q satisfy the equation $x^3 + x + 1 = 0$. Do you notice anything about these powers?

Terminology

Fields with a finite number of elements are known as Galois Fields, in honor of the young French mathematician who first investigated them, rather more than a century ago. The letters GF are used as an abbreviation for Galois Field.

$GF(2)$ is used to denote the arithmetic modulo 2, since this contains two elements 0, 1. The field with the 4 elements 0, 1, M, $M + 1$ is denoted by $GF(2^2)$. The field with 8 elements is denoted by $GF(2^3)$.

Quite generally $GF(p^n)$ denotes a Galois Field with p^n elements, where p is a prime number. (This is a slightly confusing abbreviation. In it, p^n has its usual algebraic meaning, but GF must not be interpreted algebraically as a product. GF is simply an everyday abbreviation like UNESCO or NATO.)

Chapter 7

Linear Dependence and Vector Spaces

IN CHAPTER 6, we noticed in passing that the elements of $GF(2^3)$ could be arranged in the shape of a cube, while those of $GF(2^2)$ could be arranged in a square. $GF(2)$ of course has only the two elements 0, 1 and may be visualized with the help of a line.

$$\overline{0 \qquad\qquad 1}$$

Here is a hint that fields may have some kind of geometrical aspect.

In this chapter we develop some ideas that will prove very useful for the study of fields. The language of this chapter is geometrical. "Linear" is connected with the idea of "line"; "vector," is derived from the Latin verb "to carry," and is associated with the idea of moving from one point to another. However, as was stressed in chapter 1 we are concerned with structures, not with meanings.

We shall not confine ourselves to geometrical applications, but we shall consider anything that has the same structure as certain geometrical entities. It is, in fact, very helpful to be able to pass quickly from one particular representation to another, now using a geometrical, now a numerical, now a physical realization of a structure, so that we see the analogies between all of these but are never tied to any one of them.

Let us start with a very physical example. You wish to buy some nails and screws in a hardware store. The storekeeper has observed that his customers usually buy such things for fitting hinges (using six screws) or for fixing cupboards to walls (using four screws and four nails). He has all his screws and nails done up in little packets, "The Home Handyman" with 6 screws, and "The Complete Carpenter" with 4 screws and 4 nails.

If you want to buy screws and nails for some purpose other than those envisaged by the storekeeper, and you do not want to upset the store's organization by asking to have the packets opened, there are certain limitations on what you can obtain. You can buy 26 screws and 8 nails by taking 3 Handyman packets and 2 Carpenter packets, but you certainly cannot get 3 screws and 15 nails.

Any collection of screws and nails that you are able to buy (without splitting packets) we shall call a possible purchase or, more briefly, a purchase. We shall consider purchases in their algebraic aspect, and we shall also consider how to represent them geometrically.

What algebraic operations are possible with purchases? The most obvious one is addition—the putting together of two purchases. Thus 5 Handyman and 2 Carpenter packets is a purchase; 3 Handyman and 7 Carpenter packets is another purchase. The sum of these two purchases is 8 Handyman and 9 Carpenter packets.

There is no obvious way of multiplying a purchase by a purchase. A child would know what you meant by adding a Handyman packet to a Carpenter packet, but he would be puzzled to multiply them.

There is, however, one kind of multiplication that is

possible. We know what is meant by one purchase being three times as large as another. If a purchase consists of 2 Handymans and 5 Carpenters, three times this purchase is 6 Handymans and 15 Carpenters.

Thus we can add a purchase to a purchase, but we cannot multiply a purchase by a purchase. We can however multiply a purchase by a number. This suggests a final question: can we add a number to a purchase? Imagine the following conversation.

Clerk. Is there anything else?

Customer. Yes. Three.

Clerk. Three more Carpenters, sir?

Customer. No. Just three.

Clerk. Do you want a metal three to put on your front door?

Customer. No. Just the number three.

The clerk hopes it is a harmless lunatic he is dealing with.

It is thus quite natural, in the situation described, to say

Purchase + Purchase is defined.

Number × Purchase is defined.

Purchase × Purchase is not defined.

Number + Purchase is not defined.

How arbitrary this would look in abstract formulation! "We have two sets of objects. The set P contains elements p_1, p_2, p_3, $\cdots$; the set M contains elements n_1, n_2, n_3, $\cdots$.

AXIOM 1.   *To any two elements p_1, p_2, of P there corresponds an element of P, denoted by $p_1 + p_2$.*

AXIOM 2.   *To any elements p_1 of P and n_1 of M there corresponds an element $n_1 p_1$ of P.*

"We do not, however, define products of the type $p_1 p_2$, nor sums of the type $n_1 + p_1$." Why not, you won-

der. The reasonableness of the above passage appears
as soon as you recognize P as the set of all possible purchase, and M as the set of natural numbers.

We now introduce a notation that is convenient for
our discussion of purchase, and that will have other
uses later.

Let (x, y) stand for "x screws and y nails."

Let H stand for a Handyman packet and C for a
Carpenter packet. We can then write

$$H = (6, 0) \qquad (1)$$
$$C = (4, 4) \qquad (2)$$

For the purchase that we considered earlier, consisting
of 3 Handymans and 2 Carpenters, we can write

$$3H + 2C = (26, 8) \qquad (3)$$

You can, of course, check this last equation by going
back to its meaning. However, since we are interested
in the formal aspects of this matter, we naturally try to
obtain rules for calculation with expressions of this kind.
We are guided, in making these rules, by what we know
about the meaning of the symbols.

Suppose we are given

$$F = (a, b) \qquad (4)$$
$$G = (c, d) \qquad (5)$$

How shall we find $F + G$? We go back to the meanings
of F and G.

> F stands for a screws and b nails.
> G stands for c screws and d nails.

Putting these together,

$F + G$ stands for $(a + c)$ screws and $(b + d)$ nails.

So

$$F + G = (a + c, b + d) \qquad (6)$$

f we now look at equations (4), (5), (6), we can see lat these equations give a formal definition of $F + G$.

In the same way, if n is a number, we can show that

$$n \cdot F = (na, nb) \qquad (7)$$

'his is easily justified in terms of screws and nails. But quations (4) and (7) themselves show by what rule nF s obtained from F; we can use this rule without making ny reference to the meaning of F.

raphical Interpretation

It is easy to illustrate what we have been considering vith ordinary graph paper. Some possible purchases are hown in the following diagram, the number of screws

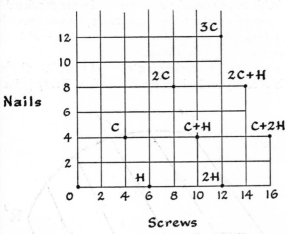

being measured horizontally and the number of nails vertically.

You will notice that, starting from any point of this et that you like, adding H always takes you 6 units to he East. Adding C always takes you a certain distance actually $4\sqrt{2}$ units) to the North-East.

This shows the relation of vectors to the word "
carry," and we could in fact explain vectors (as w.
done in the early days of vector theory) as representi
displacements. (x, y) would then stand for "x inches
the East and y inches to the North."

Clearly, if operation F sends us a inches East an
b inches North, while G sends us c inches East and d inch
North, the combined effect of F and G (one operatic
followed by the other) is to send us $(a + c)$ inches Ea
and $(b + d)$ inches North. Thus the addition procedu
defined by equations (4), (5), (6) above still holds goo
The operation F, repeated n times, will take us na inch
East and nb inches North; so this ties in well wi
equation (7).

With these operations we are no longer restricted
the natural numbers. We can have fractions and negati
numbers, with the usual understanding that $-2\frac{1}{2}$ inch
East means $2\frac{1}{2}$ inches West.

Suppose PQR represents a piece of wire. We displa
this wire say an inch to the North-East. Every point

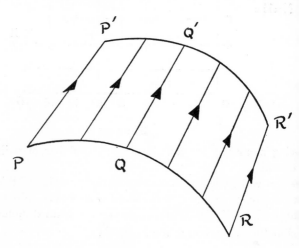

he wire moves an inch to the North-East. $P'Q'R'$ rep-
esents the final position of the wire. The arrows show
1ow each point moves. Any one of these arrows shows
1ow the whole wire moves—provided we are told that
very point undergoes the same displacement. Thus a
lisplacement can be represented by an arrow. Usually
ve draw all our arrows starting from the same point, O,
s shown below. But of course this is only a convention.

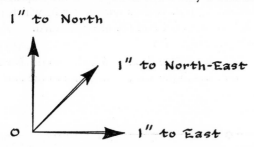

A displacement of one inch to the North" means that
very particle of a body moves one inch to the North.

Suppose we have two displacements:

F 1 inch to the East,
G 1 inch to the North-East.

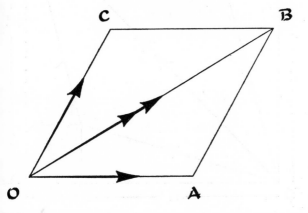

What is the combined effect of these? Consider *F*
followed by *G*. *F* would send *O* to *A*. *G* would send *A*
to *B*. The combined effect is to send *O* to *B*.

If we considered *G* followed by *F*, then *G* would send
O to *C*. *F* would send *C* to *B*. The combined effect is
again to send *O* to *B*.

Thus the combined effect of the displacements represented by the arrows *OA* and *OC* is the displacement
represented by *OB*. It does not matter in which order
the displacements *OA* and *OC* are combined.

More generally, with

F   *a* inches to the East,   *b* inches to the North,
G   *c* inches to the East,   *d* inches to the North,

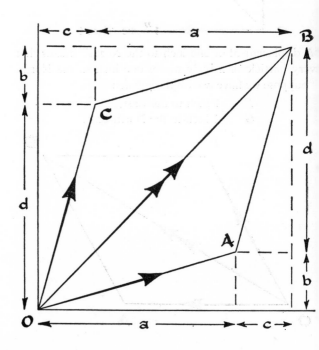

ιe arrow OA represents the displacement F, the arrow
'C represents the displacement G, the arrow OB repre-
:nts the combined effect.

We denote the combined effect by $F + G$. The par-
llelogram $OABC$ (page 137, bottom) gives us a geomet-
ical way of visualizing vector addition. The algebraic
·ay we have already had: when F is (a, b) and G is (c, d),
ιen $F + G$ is $(a + c, b + d)$. Note that this too appears
ι the figure on page 138.

Vector addition, of course, plays an important part in
ιechanics. It appears in the combination of forces,
·elocities, and accelerations. Vectors pervade many
ranches of theoretical physics—electromagnetic theory
)r instance.

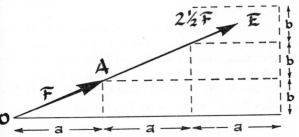

If k is a number, kF is defined as the vector (ka, kb).
'his is the vector having the same direction as F, but
:s arrow is k times as long. The diagram here shows F
ιd $2\frac{1}{2}F$. F is OA. $2\frac{1}{2}F$ is OE.

Dimension of a Space

So far we have been talking of displacements so much
) the East and so much to the North. Such displace-
ιents will get us anywhere we want on the ground.

If we want to rise in the air or bore into the ground,
·e must consider displacements a inches to the East,
inches to the North, c inches Up. Starting from a point

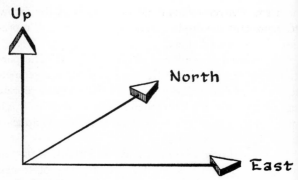

on my desk, by suitable choice of a, b, c, I can get any
where in the room. Above the desk, c will be positive
below negative. This displacement we can denote briefl
by the symbol (a, b, c).

It is still quite simple to add displacements, by con
sidering their combined effect. If I move an objec
2 inches East, 3 inches North, and 4 inches Up, and the
later I move it a farther 5 inches East, 6 inches Nort
and 8 inches Up, the total effect will be 7 inches East
9 inches North, and 12 inches Up. In symbols

> displacement A is $(2, 3, \ 4)$
> displacement B is $\underline{(5, 6, \ 8)}$
> displacement $A + B$ is $(7, 9, 12)$

The numbers in the bracket for $A + B$ are found b
three ordinary addition sums. More generally, if

$$F \text{ is } (a, b, c),$$

and

$$G \text{ is } (d, e, f),$$

then

$$F + G \text{ is } (a + d, b + e, c + f).$$

We still have to explain what we mean by kF where
k is a number.

If k is a whole number, for example 3, we expect $3F$ to mean the same as $F + F + F$. If

$$F \text{ is } (a, b, c),$$

and

$$F \text{ is } (a, b, c),$$

and

$$F \text{ is } (a, b, c),$$

then on adding,

$$F + F + F \text{ is } (3a, 3b, 3c).$$

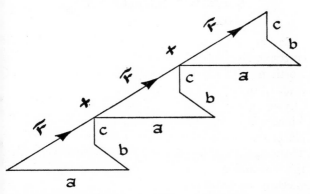

Geometrically, this is the effect of doing the displacement F three times.

In the same way, for any whole number n, it seems reasonable to say that nF means (na, nb, nc).

How about fractions? What shall we understand by $\frac{3}{5}F$? Suppose this is called X. By $X = \frac{3}{5}F$ we should naturally understand that $5X = 3F$. Now this fixes X. If X is (u, v, w), $5X$ is $(5u, 5v, 5w)$, and $3F$ is $(3a, 3b, 3c)$. This means that

$$5u = 3a, \quad 5v = 3b, \quad 5w = 3c.$$

So

$$u = \tfrac{3}{5}a, \quad v = \tfrac{3}{5}b, \quad w = \tfrac{3}{5}c.$$

Hence X is $(\tfrac{3}{5}a, \tfrac{3}{5}b, \tfrac{3}{5}c)$.

So the definition that

$$kF \text{ is } (ka, kb, kc)$$

when

$$F \text{ is } (a, b, c)$$

agrees with our ordinary ideas when k is a natural number or a positive fraction. We shall still use this definition when k is negative, like -3, or irrational, like $\sqrt{2}$.

Now let P stand for 1 inch to the East,

　　　　Q stand for 1 inch to the North,

　　　　R stand for 1 inch Up.

Earlier we had the symbol $(2, 3, 4)$ for A. What is the corresponding symbol for P? P is 1 inch East, nothing North, nothing Up. So P is $(1, 0, 0)$. In the same way, Q is $(0, 1, 0)$, and R is $(0, 0, 1)$.

Now A, being 2 inches East, 3 inches North, and 4 inches Up, could evidently be gotten by doing the displacement P twice, then Q three times, and R four times. This suggests that $A = 2P + 3Q + 4R$. We have reached this conclusion by a geometrical argument. We can check it algebraically.

Since P is $(1, 0, 0)$,　　$2P$ is $(2, 0, 0)$

Since Q is $(0, 1, 0)$,　　$3Q$ is $(0, 3, 0)$

Since R is $(0, 0, 1)$,　　$4R$ is $(0, 0, 4)$.

Adding, $2P + 3Q + 4R$ is $(2, 3, 4)$, which is A.

Exactly the same argument shows that for F, the displacement (a, b, c),

$$F = aP + bQ + cR.$$

By suitable choice of a, b, c, the vector F can be made equal to any displacement.

Thus, when we are considering displacements of this kind, any displacement can be gotten by adding suitable multiples of *three* vectors, P, Q, R. If you think of P, Q, R

as ingredients, every F can be regarded as a mixture, in suitable proportions, of these ingredients.

In our earlier work, when we did not allow displacements Up, any displacement could be gotten by a suitable mixture of P and Q. Every journey can be achieved by traveling East and then North (minus numbers accounting for West and South).

Movement on the ground—or, more generally, in a plane—is called movement in two dimensions. Movement East, North, and Up is called movement in three dimensions. In the form "3D," as applied to motion pictures, this latter term has passed into the language of the man in the street.

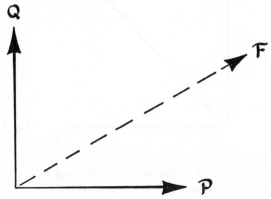

In the plane we say that P and Q form a *basis*. Different mathematicians use the word "basis" with slightly different meanings. In saying that P and Q form a basis for vectors in this plane, we shall understand the following:

(i) Every vector F can be gotten by a suitable mixture of P and Q.

(ii) Every vector F can be gotten in only one way as a mixture of P and Q,

(iii) Every mixture of P and Q lies in the plane.

To illustrate these: P by itself does not form a basis, since there are vectors in the plane that cannot be gotten by moving Eastward—algebraically, that cannot be represented by kP. For example, the vector S with components $(1, 1)$ has the direction North-East. Geometrically it is evident that S cannot be gotten by taking any amount of P (that is, by traveling East for any distance).

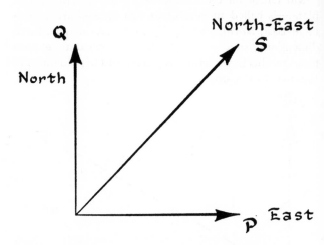

Algebraically, kP is the vector $(k, 0)$, and however we choose k we cannot make this into $(1, 1)$.

Condition (i) thus shows that P alone does not form a basis. There are more things that can be done in a plane than pure East-West travel.

Condition (ii) is intended to avoid extravagance. We might propose P, Q, and S (S was defined two paragraphs earlier) as a basis. $P + Q + S$ would then be the displacement $(1, 0) + (0, 1) + (1, 1) = (2, 2)$. But $(2, 2)$ could equally well be represented as $2S$, or as $2P + 2Q$, or as $3P + 3Q - S$, or in many other ways. As S is itself already a mixture of P and Q, it is wasteful to bring S in.

Condition (i) says, "You must have enough ingredients to give you any vector in the plane." Condition (ii) adds, in effect, "But don't be wasteful." Some discussion would be needed to prove that this is just what condition (ii) requires for the condition is not worded that way. However, if you experiment with choosing a basis for the plane, you will get the feeling that this is how it works out.

Condition (iii) is designed to avoid another kind of extravagance. P, Q, R might be proposed as a basis for displacements on the ground (P East, Q North, R Up). Now it is true that every displacement on the ground can be represented as $aP + bQ + cR$, but of course c will always have the value zero. For R takes us out of the ground plane. Condition (iii) here requires us not to include in our basis any vector that takes us out of the ground plane.

Now, of course, P, Q do not form the only basis for this plane. We could equally well take S and T as shown

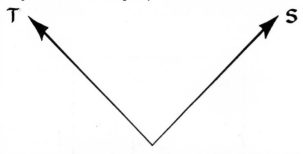

here. S, as before, is $(1, 1)$, and is to the North-East; T is $(-1, 1)$, to the North-West. A suitable combination of S and T will get us anywhere we want to go.

Nor is it necessary for the vectors in the basis to be perpendicular. A suitable combination of S and P will give us any vector F. Of course, negative numbers will be needed if F lies in certain parts of the plane. For

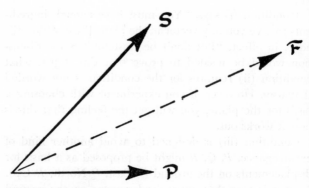

example, F might be taken as Q. How is Q to be gotten by mixing S and P?

$$S \text{ is } (1, 1),$$
$$P \text{ is } (1, 0),$$
$$Q \text{ is } (0, 1).$$

Evidently $Q = S - P$, which can also be seen geometrically. The journey S, followed by -1 to the East (1 to the West) brings us 1 to the North, as required for Q.

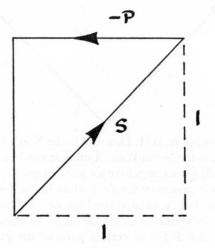

EXERCISES

1. Express S and T as mixtures of P and Q.

2. Express P and Q as mixtures of S and T. Interpret geometrically.

3. Show that the answer to question 2 could be obtained from the answer to question 1, by solving the simultaneous equations $S = P + Q$, $T = -P + Q$ for P and Q.

4. Which of the following form a basis for vectors in a plane? (i) The vectors $(0, 1)$ and $(1, 1)$. (ii) The vectors $(1, 2)$ and $(2, 1)$. (iii) The vectors $(1, 2)$ and $(2, 4)$. (iv) The vectors $(1, 5)$, $(2, 2)$, and $(4, 1)$.

5. Does any basis in the plane (i) consist of only one vector? (ii) consist of three vectors?

6. If U is (a, b) and V is (c, d), the vector (p, q) will be expressible as $xU + yV$ if x, y satisfy the equations

$$p = ax + cy$$
$$q = bx + dy.$$

Solve these equations for x and y.

If U and V form a basis, every vector (p, q) can be expressed in the form $xU + yV$. That is to say, the equations above have a solution, whatever p and q. Find the condition a, b, c, d must satisfy if this is to be so.

(If your work seems to show that the equations can always be solved, consider the case $a = 1$, $b = 1$, $c = 2$, $d = 2$. The vectors $(1, 1)$ and $(2, 2)$ do *not* form a basis. For these values the equations cannot be solved when, for example, $p = 1$, $q = 0$.)

You will have noticed that we had many ways of choosing a basis for the ground plane, but that the basis always contained two vectors—no more, no less.

In the same way, if we are allowed to move freely (North, East, and Up), we can choose as a basis the three

vectors P, Q, R. Needless to say, there are many other
ways of choosing a basis, but however we do it, we always find that it consists of three vectors. That is what we
mean when we say that we live in three dimensions, while
a creature that can only crawl on the ground is confined
to two dimensions.

Now it seems fairly evident to us that a plane is something different from a space of three dimensions. However, someone might ask us, "How do you know that
the two things are distinct? Might there not be a space
such that, by one way of choosing your basis you found
it had three vectors, and by another way you found a
basis with two vectors in it?" We certainly do not expect
such a thing to be possible; but we are now challenged
to say why. Later a theorem will be given that meets
this question.

Coefficients

In the first part of this chapter, we considered packets
of screws and nails. Since we could only buy a whole
number of packets, we considered expressions such as
$3H + 2C$ in which natural numbers came. Thus, at
this stage we considered $aH + bC$ with a, b natural
numbers. This led to the diagram on page 135, in which
the dots all lay in a certain region—between East and
North-East from the origin.

We could extend the network if we allowed a and b
to take positive or negative whole numbers as values.
Our dots would then extend in all directions, but of
course they would not fill the plane; there would still be
spaces between them, as at present.

Now we have a choice in fixing our terminology. Shall
we say that a vector space must be like a plane—a continuous membrane, so to speak—or shall we accept a

etwork of points as forming a vector space, even if here are intervals between the points?

For a book on algebra, there is no doubt about the answer. We have talked about operations $+$, $\cdot$, $-$, $\div$, but nowhere have we said what we mean by "continuous," "near to," or any such term. These are the ideas of topology or analysis rather than algebra. Provided a structure allows us to add, subtract, and multiply, we accept it.

Accordingly, we shall have a good deal of freedom in deciding what coefficients to allow. We might consider expressions $aU + bV$ where U and V were given "things" (of some kind) and a, b were required to be any one of the following:

(i) Integers (positive or negative),
(ii) Rational numbers,
(iii) Real numbers,
(iv) Complex numbers,
(v) Numbers modulo 2,
(vi) Numbers modulo 3,
(vii) Polynomials in x, with real coefficients.

This by no means exhausts the possibilities. Some of these structures we might be able to realize geometrically, others we would be unable to draw. This does not matter at all.

The following example calls attention to a possible misunderstanding. Suppose we define U as being $\sqrt{2}$ inches to the East, V as being $\sqrt{3}$ inches to the North, and require the coefficients a, b to be integers, positive or negative. This gives us a perfectly good vector space, of the "network" type. You will notice that irrational numbers $\sqrt{2}$, $\sqrt{3}$ come into the definition of U and V, while only integers are allowed for coefficients. It does not matter that $\sqrt{2}$ and $\sqrt{3}$ are not integers.

We are not doing anything worse here than when we take screws and nails as our basic "things." Here our basic "things" are an arrow pointing Eastward, and an arrow pointing Northward. One arrow happens to be $\sqrt{2}$ inches long; the other happens to be $\sqrt{3}$ inches long. We then combine a times the first arrow with b times the second arrow; a geometrical construction shows the meaning of this statement. Thus it is quite possible, in the definition of our basic "things" U, V, to use numbers that would not be acceptable as coefficients a, b.

In our hardware example, we used natural numbers as coefficients. This was quite useful as an introduction, to show how expressions like $2H + 3C$ came about. However, the natural numbers suffer from the defect that you cannot always subtract. You cannot take away 5 screws and 8 nails from 2 screws and 3 nails. In a vector space (as this term is used by the majority of mathematicians today), it is required that subtraction be always possible. That is, if L and M are two vectors, there must always be a vector X such that $L + X = M$, and X is called $M - L$. That is why the natural numbers are not on the list of suggestions for coefficients. The set of "possible purchases," mentioned at the beginning of this chapter, thus does not constitute a vector space. If we extended the definition to include negative purchases—a customer returning several packets—then it would constitute a vector space over the integers, with H and C as a basis.

Specification of a Vector Space

We have now reached the stage where we can specify what we mean by a vector space. A vector space involves two sets of objects, rather intimately mixed. I shall call these

> (i) Things,
> (ii) Numbers.

The numbers belong to a certain specified class. By the use of the word "number," I do not imply any connection with, for instance, counting. By number I just mean something that is going to be used, later on, as a coefficient like a, b above. It must be possible to add, subtract, and multiply numbers. To be more precise, I suppose the numbers to obey axioms (7) through (9), (11), and (12). (In our main applications, the numbers will be assumed to obey all the field axioms. Students should be careful to note the point in the development of the theory after which the results are true ONLY for fields.)

The set from which the numbers are drawn will be denoted by K.

There is no restriction on the kind of object that can play the role of a Thing. In any particular example, we of course specify what is allowed as a Thing. Things may be physical objects, ideas in the mind, marks on paper, sounds of words, actions, operations. A Thing can be, and usually will be, of a compound nature. Thus we regard "3 screws and 2 nails" or "5 inches East and 6 inches South" or "$3x^2 - 5xy + 6y^2$" as being a Thing. The numbers of K may very well enter into the specification of a Thing, as for example if we take

K: all real numbers.

Things: all displacements in the ground plane.

The real number $3\sqrt{2}$, for example, enters into the specification of "$3\sqrt{2}$ inches to the North-East."

The Things form a vector space of n dimensions over the numbers K if the following statements hold.

(I) Every Thing can be given a label $(a_1, a_2, \cdots, a_n)$ where $a_1, a_2, \cdots, a_n$ are numbers from K. No Thing has two different labels.

(II) To every possible label there corresponds one, and only one, Thing.

(III) Corresponding to any two Things, A and B, there is defined a third Thing, C, called the sum of A and B. If A has the label $(a_1, \cdots, a_n)$, B the label $(b_1, \cdots, b_n)$, C the label $(c_1, \cdots, c_n)$, then

$$c_1 = a_1 + b_1$$
$$c_2 = a_2 + b_2$$
$$\cdot \quad \cdot \quad \cdot \quad \cdot \quad \cdot$$
$$c_n = a_n + b_n.$$

(IV) Corresponding to any Thing A and any number k, there is defined a Thing D, called k times A. If A has the label $(a_1, \cdots, a_n)$, D has the label $(ka_1, \cdots, ka_n)$.

Some examples of vector spaces will help to make these conditions clear.

Example 1.

K: the real numbers.

Things: the displacements in the ground plane.

We use (a, b) as a label for "a inches East and b inches North." This provides a label for every possible displacement. There is a displacement corresponding to every possible label. We never get two different labels for the same displacement, nor two different displacements for the same label.

We have already seen how statements (III) and (IV) apply. We have here a space of 2 dimensions over the real numbers.

Example 2.

K: the integers.

Things: all expressions $ax + by + cz$ with whole number coefficients a, b, c.

Addition of expressions and multiplication of expressions by numbers are defined as in elementary algebra.

Thus, for example, the sum of $2x + 3y + 4z$ and $5x + 6y + 7z$ is $7x + 9y + 11z$; and 5 times $2x + 3y + 4z$ is $10x + 15y + 20z$.

We choose the label (a, b, c) for the expression $ax + by + cz$. Thus $(2, 3, 4)$ is the label for $2x + 3y + 4z$. No other expression gets this label. No expression has two different labels.

Does statement (III) apply?

We take an example:

$$2x + 3y + 4z \text{ has label } (2, 3, 4),$$
$$5x + 6y + 7z \text{ has label } (5, 6, 7).$$

If statement (III) holds, the sum should have label $(7, 9, 11)$.

In fact, it does so. One can show, by simple algebra, that statement (III) applies generally.

Does statement (IV) hold? Again, we take an example. The expression $2x + 3y + 4z$ has label $(2, 3, 4)$. If statement (IV) holds, 5 times the expression should have label $(10, 15, 20)$. It does; and we can show that this always happens.

We have here a vector space of 3 dimensions over the integers. Every expression $ax + by + cz$ is a mixture of x, y, and z. x, y, z form a basis. You may notice that x has the label $(1, 0, 0)$, y the label $(0, 1, 0)$; z the label $(0, 0, 1)$.

Example 3.

K: the real numbers.
Things: all quadratics $ax^2 + bx + c$ with real a, b, c.

This is a vector space of 3 dimensions over the real numbers. x^2, x, 1 form a basis. $ax^2 + bc + c$ receives the label (a, b, c). x^2 has the label $(1, 0, 0)$, x the label $(0, 1, 0)$, 1 the label $(0, 0, 1)$.

Example 4.

K: the rational numbers.

Things: all numbers $a + b\sqrt{2}$ with a, b rational.

We assign the label (a, b) to $a + b\sqrt{2}$. Thus $5 + 7\sqrt{2}$ would be labeled $(5, 7)$. It is clear that only one Thing, $a + b\sqrt{2}$, corresponds to the label (a, b). But what about the other way? Can two different labels give the same Thing? Suppose they could; imagine that (a, b) and (c, d) are two labels for the same Thing. This means that

$$a + b\sqrt{2} = c + d\sqrt{2},$$
$$a - c = (d - b)\sqrt{2}.$$

If $d - b$ is not zero, we can divide by it. Then

$$(a - c)/(d - b) = \sqrt{2}.$$

This gives $\sqrt{2}$ as a fraction, a rational number. But this has been proved impossible. So $d - b$ must be zero. It follows that $a - c$ is zero also. Hence $d = b$, $a = c$. So the two labels are the same.

Statements (III) and (IV) can be checked without difficulty. We thus have a vector space of 2 dimensions over the rationals: 1 has the label $(1, 0)$, $\sqrt{2}$ the label $(0, 1)$. Together 1 and $\sqrt{2}$ form a basis.

Example 5.

K: 0, 1 modulo 2
Things: 0, 1, M, $M + 1$.

The Things here form $GF(2^2)$. All the Things are obtained by letting a and b run through the values 0, 1 in the expression $a + bM$. We have a vector space of 2 dimensions over K.

1 has the label $(1, 0)$, and M the label $(0, 1)$.
1, M form a basis.

Example 6.

$$K: \text{ the integers.}$$
$$\text{Things: } a + \tfrac{1}{2}b, \ (a, b \text{ integers}).$$

This has perhaps the appearance of a space of 2 dimensions with (a, b) as the label for $a + \tfrac{1}{2}b$. But then $(3, 0)$, $(2, 2)$, $(1, 4)$, $(0, 6)$, and many others would all label the same thing.

In fact, of course, whatever integers you choose for a, b, the value of $a + \tfrac{1}{2}b$ will lie in the set

$$\cdots, -1\tfrac{1}{2}, -1, -\tfrac{1}{2}, 0, \tfrac{1}{2}, 1, 1\tfrac{1}{2}, 2, \cdots$$

These are all of the form $\tfrac{1}{2}m$ where m is an integer. We have a space of 1 dimension over the integers. Basis, the single Thing, $\tfrac{1}{2}$. (m) is the label for $\tfrac{1}{2}m$.

Contrast example 4.

Example 7.

$$K: \text{ the integers.}$$
$$\text{Things: all numbers of the form } a^b$$
$$\text{where } a, b \text{ are integers.}$$
$$\text{Sum and product: as in arithmetic.}$$

This, of course, is not a vector space over the integers. If b is positive, a^b is an integer. If b is negative, say $b = -m$, then $a^b = a^{-m} = 1/a^m$ and a^b is the reciprocal of an integer.

Now $3^{-1} = 1/3$ and $5^{-1} = 1/5$, but $3^{-1} + 5^{-1} = 1/3 + 1/5 = 8/15$, which is neither an integer nor the reciprocal of an integer. So $A = 3^{-1}$, $B = 5^{-1}$ are Things, but $A + B$ is not a Thing.

There is another way in which this structure fails to be a vector space that is worth noting. Suppose we decided to take (a, b) as a label for a^b.

a^b gets the label (a, b),

c^d gets the label (c, d).

If statement (III) holds, $a^b + c^d$ ought to get the label $(a + c, b + d)$, but $a^b + c^d$ is not equal to $(a + c)^{(b+d)}$.

Chapter 8

Algebraic Calculations
with Vectors

WE SAW in Example 2 (page 153) that linear expressions of the form $ax + by + cz$ constituted a vector space of 3 dimensions. Thus a vector space is no unfamiliar thing; if you have handled linear expressions in school algebra, you already know a vector space and how it behaves. But, more than this, vector spaces have very little individuality; they differ of course in dimension, but this is not a very serious difference—if you can correctly perform algebraic calculations on expressions of the type $ax + by + cz$, you will hardly find difficulties with the type $ax + by$ or the type $ax + by + cz + dt$. Vector spaces also differ in the numbers K they employ: it makes some difference whether a, b, c are integers, or rational, or real, or numbers modulo 5—but again, not very much difference; algebraic calculations with all of these have much in common. *Working with vector spaces is accordingly much the same thing as working with linear expressions in elementary algebra.*

You may have noticed that all the equations we have had connecting vectors have been linear equations, for example:

$$F = aP + bQ + cR \quad \text{(page 142)}$$
$$Q = S - P \quad \text{(page 146)}$$

Linear expressions are very simple to handle. Geometrical questions, which otherwise might be difficult, can sometimes be expressed in the language of vectors, and thus converted into simple algebraic problems.

Example. Three wires radiate from a point O. The first wire is horizontal and points due East. The second wire makes an angle of 45° with the horizontal and goes North from O. The third wire goes in a Northeasterly direction, and rises 1 foot for every $\sqrt{2}$ feet in a horizontal direction. Do the three wires lie in a plane or not?

Solution. We use the symbol (a, b, c) as on page 140. The first wire evidently has the same direction as the vector $(1, 0, 0) = A$, say. The second wire has the direction of the vector $(0, 1, 1) = B$, say. The third wire has the direction of the vector $(1, 1, 1) = C$, say. (A diagram or model will make these statements clear.)

Does C lie in the plane of A and B? To answer this question we must translate into the language of vectors "the plane of A and B." This is not hard to do.

If we go any distance in the direction of A, and then

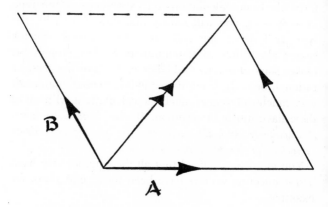

any distance in the direction of B, the total displacement is one lying in the plane of A and B.

The vector corresponding to "any distance in the direction of A" is represented by sA, for some number s.

The vector corresponding to "any distance in the direction of B" is represented by tB, for some number t.

The combined effect of these displacements is gotten by addition (see page 139). It is thus $sA + tB$.

Hence any vector in the plane of A and B is of the form $sA + tB$.

Our question becomes, can we find numbers s and t for which $C = sA + tB$?

This question can in fact be answered immediately. We have

$$A = (1, 0, 0),$$
$$B = (0, 1, 1),$$
$$A + B = (1, 1, 1) = C.$$

So $s = 1$, $t = 1$ does the trick.

If we did not spot this, we should have to proceed as follows:

$$A = (1, 0, 0). \therefore sA = (s, 0, 0).$$
$$B = (0, 1, 1). \therefore tB = (0, t, t).$$
$$\therefore sA + tB = (s, t, t).$$

We want, if possible, to make this equal to $(1, 1, 1)$. $s = 1$, $t = 1$ does this.

So the three wires do lie in one plane.

The connection of this work with linear expressions appears most clearly if we use the three vectors P, Q, R as defined on page 142. (The symbols A, B we are now using have of course no connection with the symbols A, B occurring on pages 139–142.) Then

$$A = P$$
$$B = Q + R$$
$$C = P + Q + R$$

and the question is, can we find numbers s, t so that $C = sA + tB$? To see that $s = 1$, $t = 1$ provides a solution requires no knowledge beyond very elementary algebra.

Someone who was told to handle vector expressions $aP + bQ + cR$ "just like $ax + by + cz$ in elementary algebra" would probably find this quite a sufficient guide for practical calculation. However, this prescription is somewhat vague, and it will be as well to list the properties we have in mind.

For definiteness, we shall take $n = 4$, so that our vectors will have labels (a_1, a_2, a_3, a_4). But the arguments apply equally well whatever natural number is chosen for n.

The numbers, shown by small letters, a_1, b_2, k, and so on, are supposed to obey axioms (1) through (9) and (11). The vectors, or "Things," are subject to statements (I)–(IV) of page 152.

Denote by P_1 the vector with the label $(1, 0, 0, 0)$,
Denote by P_2 the vector with the label $(0, 1, 0, 0)$,
Denote by P_3 the vector with the label $(0, 0, 1, 0)$,
Denote by P_4 the vector with the label $(0, 0, 0, 1)$.

It requires no ingenuity to verify the results listed below. Several of these are left as exercises.

(V.1) Corresponding to any two vectors, A and B, there is a vector C, called $A + B$. This is given in statement (III), page 152.

(V.2) $A + B = B + A$. This follows from the latter part of statement (III), and from axiom (3) for numbers a_r, b_r.

(V.3) $A + (B + C) = (A + B) + C$.

(V.4) There is a vector O such that $A + O = A$ for any vector A.

(V.5) The equation $A + X = B$ has a unique solution X, whatever the vectors A and B. X is called $B - A$.

(V.6) For any number k and any vector A, the product $k \cdot A$ is uniquely defined. This is the earlier part of statement (IV).

(V.7) For any number k and any vectors A, B,

$$k \cdot (A + B) = (k \cdot A) + (k \cdot B).$$

(V.8) For any numbers a, b and for any vector A,

$$(a + b) \cdot A = (a \cdot A) + (b \cdot A).$$

(V.9) For any numbers a, b and for any vector A,

$$(ab) \cdot A = a \cdot (b \cdot A)$$

(V.10) Every vector A is expressible in the form

$$a_1 P_1 + a_2 P_2 + a_3 P_3 + a_4 P_4.$$

(This is for $n = 4$. In general, $a_1 P_1 + \cdots + a_n P_n$ of course replaces the expression here.)

EXERCISES

1. Prove statements (V.3, V.4, V.5, V.7, V.8, V.9, V.10) above, the statements (I)–(IV) of page 152, and the axioms (1)–(9) and (11) for the numbers being given as known.

2. Prove from the statements (V.1)–(V.10), that for the vector O and for any number k, we have $k \cdot O = O$.

3. Prove that, if 1 is the unit of the number system, for any vector A, we have $1 \cdot A = A$. (Begin with V.10. Use V.7 and V.9.)

4. Prove that, 0 denoting the zero of the number system, and A being any vector, we have $0 \cdot A = O$.

5. Prove that, if $-A$ is used as an abbreviation for $O - A$, then $-A = (-1) \cdot A$.

6. What statements from (V.1)–(V.10) are used in obtaining the following results? (i) $2 \cdot (3A + 4B) + 5 \cdot (3A + 4B) = 7 \cdot (3A + 4B)$. (ii) $3 \cdot (5A + 6B) = 15A + 18B$.

The above examples show how closely calculations with vectors resemble elementary algebra; in fact, as was mentioned earlier, linear expressions $ax + by + cz + dt$ actually constitute a vector space.

Thus, in order to work with vectors, no new formula, no new procedure needs to be memorized.

Statements (I) through (IV) of page 152 are needed if one is in doubt whether or not some particular structure is a vector space.

Statements (V.1) through (V.10) resemble several of the axioms for a field (page 27). Of course, they contain nothing resembling field axiom *(10)*, that provides for division. These statements, (V.1) through (V.10), can always be appealed to, if our right to perform some formal algebraic manipulation with vectors is challenged, or if we are in doubt whether or not a particular step is justified. In some treatments of vector spaces, statements (V.1) through (V.10) form the starting point, rather than statements (I) through (IV).

Linear Independence

Suppose, in elementary algebra, we consider all expressions of the form $au + bv + cw$, where a, b, c are integers and

$$u = x + y + z + t,$$
$$v = x + 2y + 3z + 4t,$$
$$w = x + 4y + 7z + 10t.$$

At first sight, you might think these expressions constituted a vector space of 3 dimensions, basis u, v, w, with (a, b, c) as the label for the expression $au + bv + cw$.

However, consider the two cases

$$\text{(i)} \quad a = 1 \quad b = 5 \quad c = 3,$$
$$\text{(ii)} \quad a = 3 \quad b = 2 \quad c = 4.$$

We find

$$u + 5v + 3w = 9x + 23y + 37z + 51t,$$
$$3u + 2v + 4w = 9x + 23y + 37z + 51t.$$

That is to say, the labels $(1, 5, 3)$ and $(3, 2, 4)$ both describe the same Thing. This, however, is contrary to statement (I). Since

$$u + 5v + 3w = 3u + 2v + 4w,$$

it follows that

$$2u - 3v + w = 0. \tag{1}$$

In fact, $w = -2u + 3v$, so any expression $au + bv + cw$ could be written $au + bv + c(-2u + 3v)$. This equals $(a - 2c)u + (b + 3c)v$, which is a mixture of u and v alone. For example, $u + 5v + 3w$ and $3u + 2v + 4w$ above are both expressible as $-5u + 14v$.

Thus it now appears that we have a vector space of only 2 dimensions, with u, v as a basis. But perhaps this is not yet the end of the story; perhaps u, v can be replaced by something even simpler. We now examine this possibility.

Suppose we use (a, b) as the label for the expression $au + bv$. Can one expression receive two labels? Suppose it could; suppose (p, q) and (r, s) represented the same expression, that is,

$$pu + qv = ru + sv. \tag{2}$$

Then

$$(p - r)u + (q - s)v = 0.$$

We write

$$f = p - r$$
$$g = q - s \tag{3}$$

So

$$fu + gv = 0. \tag{4}$$

Now

$$u = x + y + z + t,$$
$$v = x + 2y + 3z + 4t.$$

For $fu + gv$ to be zero, we must have (as is seen by considering the coefficients of x, y, z, t)

$$f + g = 0$$
$$f + 2g = 0$$
$$f + 3g = 0 \tag{5}$$
$$f + 4g = 0$$

The only solution of these simultaneous equations is $f = 0$, $g = 0$. By equations (3), this means that $p = r$, $q = s$. And this means that (p, q) and (r, s) are one and the same label.

So it is impossible for one expression to receive two distinct labels. With u, v as a basis, all the requirements of statements (I)–(IV) are met, and our expressions thus form a vector space of 2 dimensions.

In this investigation, one or two ideas have occurred that are of value for the theory generally, so that it is worth while to introduce names for them.

In testing whether u, v formed a basis for a space of 2 dimensions, we considered the mixture $fu + gv$. We found that this was zero only when both f and g were zero. The only way of mixing u and v so as to obtain zero was to take none of either.

We then say that u, v are *linearly independent*.

Generally, we say that n vectors $u_1, u_2, \cdots, u_n$ are linearly independent if the only way to make the mixture $c_1u_1 + c_2u_2 + \cdots + c_nu_n$ zero is to make $c_1 = 0$, $c_2 = 0$, $\cdots$, $c_n = 0$.

On the other hand, we had above u, v, w for which the mixture $2u - 3v + w$ was zero. This is a genuine mixture; it is not just "none of u, none of v, none of w." Accordingly, we say that u, v, w are *linearly dependent*.

DEFINITION. *If n vectors, u_1, u_2, $\cdots$, u_n satisfy a linear equation,*

$$c_1 u_1 + c_2 u_2 + \cdots + c_n u_n = 0,$$

other than the trivial equation,

$$0 u_1 + 0 u_2 + \cdots + 0 u_n = 0,$$

which is satisfied by any set of n vectors, we call the vectors "linearly dependent."

You will notice that "linearly independent" is another way of saying "not linearly dependent." A set of vectors, u_1, $\cdots$, u_n, must be one or the other.

Geometrical Interpretation

Geometrical examples of vector fields are helpful for illustrating the meaning of linear independence.

For instance, on page 142 we met vectors P, Q, R which represented an inch to the East, an inch to the North, and an inch Up, respectively. Are these linearly independent or not? That is, can we find a genuine mixture of them that is zero? If we take $c_1 P + c_2 Q + c_3 R$, this represents the displacement c_1 inches to the East, c_2 inches to the North, c_3 inches Upwards. It is clear that this gives the zero displacement only if $c_1 = c_2 = c_3 = 0$. That is, only the trivial mixture gives zero. Hence P, Q, R are linearly independent.

If, on the other hand, we take the vectors P, Q, S of page 144, we have $P + Q - S = 0$. The vectors are linearly dependent.

Quite generally, if U, V, W are three vectors in geometrical space of 3 dimensions, they are linearly dependent if they satisfy a non-trivial equation.

$$aU + bV + cW = 0.$$

Then the journey aU (which is in the same direction as

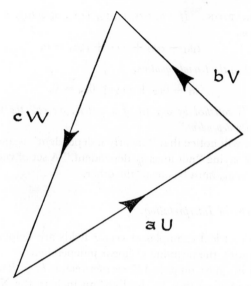

U), followed by the journey bV and the journey cW, brings us back to the point where we started. Evidently this means that U, V, W lie in a plane.

EXERCISES

By a model or diagram make clear to yourself how the vectors listed below are situated in space. Hence determine whether or not each set is linearly independent. *Check your conclusions algebraically.*

1. $A = (1, 1, 0)$, $B = (-1, 1, 0)$, $C = (0, 0, 1)$.
2. $A = (2, 3, 0)$, $B = (10, 1, 0)$, $C = (1, 1, 0)$.
3. $A = (0, 1, -1)$, $B = (-1, 0, 1)$, $C = (1, -1, 0)$.
4. $A = (0, 1, 1)$, $B = (1, 0, 1)$, $C = (1, 1, 0)$.

Chapter 9

Vectors Over a Field

———————

THE PROCESSES we are soon to use involve division by a number. *From now on, we assume that our number system forms a field.*

On page 159 we saw that the vectors of a plane were all of the form $sA + tB$.

In the same way, all the vectors that lie in a line are of the form sA. Those that fill a 3-dimensional space are of the form $sA + tB + pC$.

It is thus natural to study mixtures of a given set of vectors. We may in this way obtain vector spaces that do not correspond to our geometrical ideas derived from the physical world. By considering mixtures of linear expressions in ten variables we could construct, algebraically, vector spaces of any number up to 10 dimensions. Needless to say, we cannot visualize such spaces geometrically, though we may be helped in dealing with them by analogies drawn from our physical experience of three dimensions. Vectors in such spaces are not without practical interest. In intelligence testing, for instance, a candidate might be subjected to ten examinations. If candidate A scored $(a_1, a_2, \cdots, a_{10})$ in these examinations, his performance would specify a vector in 10 dimensions. If candidate B scored $b_1, \cdots, b_{10}$ and candidate C scored $c_1, \cdots, c_{10}$, one might find, perhaps, that in each test C's score was the sum of A's and B's. This we could write as $C = A + B$. Or C's marks might be, in each examination, the average of A's and B's. Or again, if A scored full marks on test 1, and almost nothing on the others while B scored high marks on test 10 and nothing on the others, we could say that A's and B's abilities lay *in different directions*. All of this goes quite naturally in the language of vectors, and in fact vectors are used considerably in the theories of intelligence. We are, then, concerned with mixtures of vectors, whether these can be illustrated in physical terms or not.

We saw on page 163 that a mixture of three vectors might sometimes produce a vector space of only 2 dimensions. It is desirable to have a systematic way of determining the dimensions of the space generated by a collection of vectors. (The space formed by all possible mixtures of a given set of vectors is said to be generated by these vectors.) This is quite simple to do. The process depends on the two following principles.

PRINCIPLE I.   *The space generated by a set of vectors is unaltered if any vector P is replaced by kP, where k is any non-zero number.*

PRINCIPLE II.   *The space generated by a set of vectors is unaltered if any two vectors P, Q of the set are replaced by P, $Q - sP$ where s is any number whatever.*

Principle I, applied to a set of three vectors A, B, C, states that kA, B, C generate the same space; that is, any mixture of kA, B, C is a mixture of A, B, C, and conversely. That a mixture of kA, B, C is a mixture of A, B, C is almost obvious. That a mixture of A, B, C can always be expressed as a mixture of kA, B, C appears from the equation

$$aA + bB + cC = (a/k) \cdot (kA) + bB + cC.$$

No new idea is needed to prove this principle for any number of vectors.

The way in which principle II is proved is also clear from the particular case of three vectors. We want to show that P, Q, R and P, $Q - sP$, R generate the same space. We write

$$U = P,$$
$$V = Q - sP,$$
$$W = R.$$

It is to be shown that any mixture of U, V, W is a mixture of P, Q, R, and conversely. That a mixture of U, V, W is a mixture of P, Q, R is obvious. But since

$$P = U,$$
$$Q = V + sU,$$
$$R = W,$$

it is also obvious that any mixture of P, Q, R is expressible as a mixture of U, V, W.

The proof for any number of vectors follows exactly the same lines.

Principle II can be applied repeatedly. For instance, by applying it three times, one can see that (P, Q, R, S) and $(P, Q - aP, R - bP, S - cP)$ generate the same space.

Great caution is needed to avoid jumping to unwarranted conclusions. One might think that P, Q, R and $P - Q$, $Q - R$, $R - P$ would generate the same space. This, however, cannot be derived by any number of applications of principle II, and is in fact untrue; consider for example the case when P, Q, R are all equal.

Conditions for a Space of n Dimensions

Suppose now we take any n vectors $P_1, P_2, \cdots, P_n$, and consider all the vectors of the form $a_1P_1 + a_2P_2 + \cdots +$

a_nP_n. Do these form a space of n dimensions? Conditions (II), (III), (IV) of page 152 are automatically satisfied, $(a_1, a_2, \cdots, a_n)$ being regarded as the label for $a_1P_1 + a_2P_2 + \cdots + a_nP_n$. The only doubt is in regard to the latter sentence in condition (I). As we saw in the example on page 163, this can fail: two different labels may correspond to the same thing.

What is the condition for this failure? If $(a_1, \cdots, a_n)$ and $(b_1, \cdots, b_n)$ are two labels for the same vector, this means that

$$a_1P_1 + a_2P_2 + \cdots + a_nP_n = b_1P_1 + b_2P_2 + \cdots + b_nP_n,$$

whence

$$(a_1 - b_1)\cdot P_1 + (a_2 - b_2)\cdot P_2 + \cdots + (a_n - b_n)\cdot P_n = 0.$$

Now $(a_1, \cdots, a_n)$ is not the same as $(b_1, \cdots, b_n)$. This means that at least one of the coefficients above is not zero. Hence, $P_1, P_2, \cdots, P_n$ are linearly dependent, for they satisfy a non-trivial equation (see definition, page 165).

Accordingly, if $P_1, \cdots, P_n$ are linearly *in*dependent, the failure of condition (I) cannot occur. All the conditions (I)–(IV) are then satisfied, and we have the following theorem.

THEOREM. *If $P_1, \cdots, P_n$ are n linearly independent vectors, they generate a space of n dimensions; that is, the totality of vectors of the form $a_1P_1 + \cdots + a_nP_n$ constitute a space of n dimensions.*

A Standard Form

We now consider two examples in which it is immediately evident that a set of vectors are linearly independent. These examples are significant. It will be shown later that *any* set of vectors can be reduced to this form by means of principles I and II.

Example. What is the dimension of the space generated by P, Q, R, S here specified?

$$P = x + 4y - 17z + 3t - 2u,$$
$$Q = \quad\quad v + 5z - 81t + 39u,$$
$$R = \quad\quad\quad\quad z + 4t + 111u,$$
$$S = \quad\quad\quad\quad\quad\quad t - 13u.$$

By the theorem above, we shall be sure that the space is of 4 dimensions, if we can prove P, Q, R, S linearly independent.

Suppose P, Q, R, S satisfy an equation

$$aP + bQ + cR + dS = 0.$$

Consider the coefficient of x. x appears only once on the left-hand side in the term ax. Hence, $a = 0$. Accordingly,

$$bQ + cR + dS = 0.$$

Now y appears only in the term by. Hence, $b = 0$. We substitute $b = 0$ in the equation, and go on to consider the coefficient of z. This shows $c = 0$. Finally, from the coefficient of t, we see $d = 0$.

Hence, P, Q, R, S satisfy only the trivial equation with all coefficients zero. Hence, by definition, they are linearly independent. So the space generated by P, Q, R, S is of 4 dimensions.

You will notice in this example that the coefficients ($4, -17, 3, -2$ in P; $5, -81, 39$ in Q; $4, 111$ in R; -13 in S) are never mentioned in the proof. The proof depends only on the fact that the non-zero coefficients form the following pattern.

$$
\begin{array}{ccccc}
1 & * & * & * & * \\
  & 1 & * & * & * \\
  &   & 1 & * & * \\
  &   &   & 1 & * \\
\end{array}
$$

It is also possible to have examples in which the pattern

shows steps rather than a diagonal edge, for example
the following.

1	*	*	*	*	*	*	*
	1	*	*	*	*	*	
		1	*	*	*		
			1				

Question: Show that a space of 4 dimensions is generated by the vectors P, Q, R, S where

$$
\begin{aligned}
P &= x + y + z + t + u + v + w + s, \\
Q &= \phantom{x + y + z + {}} t + 2u + 2v + 2w + 2s, \\
R &= \phantom{x + y + z + t + 2u + {}} v + 3w + 3s, \\
S &= \phantom{x + y + z + t + 2u + 2v + 3w + {}} s.
\end{aligned}
$$

In example 2 on page 153, we saw that the label
(a, b, c) can be attached to the expression $ax + by + cz$.
Our two examples above could equally well be expressed
by means of such labels.

Thus, the first example would show that a space of
4 dimensions is generated by the vectors

$$
\begin{aligned}
(1, &\quad 4, \quad -17, \quad\;\; 3, \quad -2), \\
(0, &\quad 1, \quad\;\;\; 5, \quad -81, \quad 39), \\
(0, &\quad 0, \quad\;\;\; 1, \quad\;\;\; 4, \quad 111), \\
(0, &\quad 0, \quad\;\;\; 0, \quad\;\;\; 1, \quad -13).
\end{aligned}
$$

It is good to be able to follow the argument in either
form of notation. It is, of course, essentially the same
argument in either notation. One can pass from a question stated in bracket notation—that is, with signs such
as $(a, b, \cdots, k)$—to the linear expression notation, by the
process used on page 159.

In the two examples we have just had, we may say
that the system P, Q, R, S is in *standard form*. In the first
example, P contains the symbol x, which is not in any
later expression Q, R, S. Q contains y, which is not in
R, S. R contains z, which is not in S. S contains t. (S is

not followed by any expression. So all we require of S here is that it should not be identically zero. If it were identically zero, we should simply omit it, since it would make no contribution to the space.)

In the second example, P contains x, which is not in any later expression Q, R, S. Q contains t, not in R, S. R contains v, not in S. And S contains s.

These remarks should convey what is meant by "standard form."

EXERCISES

1. Define formally when n linear expressions $X_1, \cdots, X_n$ in m symbols $x_1, \cdots, x_m$ are in standard form.

2. Make clear to yourself how you would recognize that n vectors expressed in bracket notation were in standard form. (The verbal definition of such a property is often difficult and tedious. The idea of standard form can certainly be grasped by students who are unable to formulate it verbally. For our purposes, the ability to *recognize* standard form is important; the verbalization, less so.)

Reduction to Standard Form

Our principles I and II allow us to make chains of arguments such as the following:

Space generated by A, B, C
$\quad$ = space generated by A, $B - 2A$, C $\qquad$ by (II)
$\quad$ = space generated by A, $B - 2A$, $C - 3A$ $\quad$ by (II).

We thus move from the set of vectors A, B, C to the set A, $B - 2A$, C to the set A, $B - 2A$, $C - 3A$. These sets of vectors are of course distinct. We could not write that these sets were equal. But they have the property that they generate the same space.

Accordingly, when we speak of reducing a set of vectors to standard form, this is a brief way of saying that we are looking for another set, a simpler set, *that generate the same space* as the original set. For example, if

$$A = x + 5y + 12z,$$
$$B = 2x + 11y + 33z,$$
$$C = 3x + 9y + z,$$

the argument above leads us to

$$A = x + 5y + 12z$$
$$D = B - 2A = \quad y + 9z$$
$$E = C - 3A = \quad -6y - 35z.$$

A, D, E generate the same space as A, B, C. Now A, D, E are not yet a standard set. But they are nearer to standard form than A, B, C since x occurs in A but not in B, C.

To complete the reduction to standard form, we apply principle **II** again, and replace (A, D, E) by $(A, D, E + 6D)$. This yields

$$A = x + 5y + 12z,$$
$$D = \quad y + 9z,$$
$$F = E + 6D = \quad 19z.$$

Finally, by principle **I**, the expressions A, D, F can be replaced by $A, D, F/19$, and standard form is thus attained.

$$A = x + 5y + 12z,$$
$$D = \quad y + 9z,$$
$$G = \quad z.$$

A, B, C generate the same space as A, D, G; evidently this is a space of 3 dimensions.

Question: There is an even simpler set of three vectors that generates this space. What is it?

The procedure followed in reduction to standard form

should be clear. First we select a symbol (x) that actually occurs in A. By "actually occurs" I mean that its coefficient is not zero. Suppose, then, that A contains the term ax. By principle I, we can replace A by $(1/a) \cdot A$. We thus have an expression

$$P = (1/a) \cdot A = x + \cdots.$$

If B contains bx, we replace B by $B - bP$, which does not contain x. In the same way, we can replace C, containing cx, by $C - cP$, which contains no x.

Thus we arrive at a set P, Q, R, S, $\cdots$, in which P alone contains x. We set P on one side. We can now forget about x, since Q, R, S, $\cdots$, do not contain it. We choose a symbol y that actually occurs in Q, and follow the same kind of procedure to replace R, S, $\cdots$, by expressions free from y. We continue until a standard form is reached.

Example. Reduce A, B, C to standard form, where

$$
\begin{aligned}
A &= x + y + z + 2t + u, \\
B &= 2x + 5y + 8z + 7t + 5u, \\
C &= x + 2y + 4z + 2t - u.
\end{aligned}
$$

A contains x. We subtract from B and C multiples of A so chosen that x disappears. We thus reach

$$
\begin{aligned}
A &= x + y + z + 2t + u, \\
D = B - 2A &= 3y + 6z + 3t + 3u, \\
E = C - A &= y + 3z - 2u.
\end{aligned}
$$

The coefficient of y in D is 3. So we use principle I and consider $\frac{1}{3}D$. (It does not matter if such a step introduces fractions. We are working with the *field* of rationals. Actually, no fractions occur in this example.)

$$
\begin{aligned}
A &= x + y + z + 2t + u, \\
F = \tfrac{1}{3}D &= y + 2z + t + u, \\
E &= y + 3z - 2u.
\end{aligned}
$$

Finally, we have

$$A = x + y + z + 2t + u,$$
$$F = \quad\quad y + 2z + t + u,$$
$$G = E - F = \quad\quad\quad z - t - 3u,$$

which is in standard form.

Example. Reduce to standard form the expressions u, v, w of page 162. These expressions, you may remember, generated a space of only 2 dimensions. We shall see how this appears in the work.

$$u = x + y + z + t,$$
$$v = x + 2y + 3z + 4t,$$
$$w = x + 4y + 7z + 10t.$$

x occurs in the top row. We use principle II to get rid of it in the other rows.

$$u = x + y + z + t,$$
$$p = v - u = \quad\quad y + 2z + 3t,$$
$$q = w - u = \quad\quad 3y + 6z + 9t.$$

y occurs in p. We get rid of y in the third row by forming $q - 3p$. This, however, is $0y + 0z + 0t$, the vector zero. It makes no contribution to the space generated, and is accordingly omitted. Thus the standard form is

$$u = x + y + z + t,$$
$$p = \quad\quad y + 2z + 3t.$$

The two vectors u, p generate the same space as the original three vectors u, v, w.

The fact that $q - 3p$ is zero shows that u, v, w are linearly dependent. For $q = w - u$, and $p = v - u$. Substituting for p and q we obtain

$$0 = q - 3p = (w - u) - 3(v - u),$$
$$= 2u - 3v + w,$$

as in equation (1) of page 163.

EXERCISES

Reduce the following systems to standard form. Whenever a
zero vector appears in the work, verify that the corresponding
vector in the original system is a mixture of the vectors which
precede it. (In our last example, the third vector in the process
of reduction is zero; this corresponds to the fact that the third
vector, w, of the original system u, v, w can be expressed as
$-2u + 3v$.) Find the relationship in each system.

1. $A = x + y + z,$
   $B = x + 3y + 3z + 2t,$
   $C = 2x + 3y + 6z + 4t + 3u.$

2. $A = x + 2y + 3z + 4t,$
   $B = 5x + 6y + 7z + 8t,$
   $C = 9x + 10y + 11z + 12t,$
   $D = 13x + 14y + 15z + 16t.$

3. $A = x - 2y + z,$
   $B = x + y - 2z,$
   $C = -2x + y + z.$

4. $A = x - y,$
   $B = y - z,$
   $C = -x + z.$

5. $A = x + y,$
   $B = y + z,$
   $C = x + z.$

We have had several examples in which the appearance of a zero vector in the reduction process indicated
that a vector of the original system was a mixture of the
preceding vectors. We have not, however, proved that
this must be so.

The proof requires only one point to be established.
In our worked example on page 176, we had $q - 3p = 0$.

p and q were linear expressions in the original symbols u, v, w. It seems evident that substitution for p and q in terms of u, v, w must give a relation $au + bv + cw = 0$. There is, however, one loophole that must be filled; it might be that a, b, c all happen to be zero. In that event we have not shown u, v, w to be linearly dependent.

In actual fact $q - 3p = 2u - 3v + w$ and the coefficient of w is 1. This is no accident. The process we have described is such that *the coefficient of the last vector involved is bound to be 1*. This by itself is sufficient to show that we are not dealing with the trivial equation where all coefficients are zero.

We still have to establish the statement just made, that the coefficient is 1.

For definiteness, let us suppose that in the reduction of A, B, C, D, $\cdots$, a zero vector appears at the third step. We review the process of reduction. Let a, b, c, d, $\cdots$, stand for numbers that appear in the work. *These have no connection with any symbols previously used.*

We suppose A contains x, perhaps not with coefficient 1, but with non-zero coefficient. We can make the coefficient of x become 1 by multiplying with a suitable constant a. Thus $aA = x + \cdots$.

We now subtract suitable multiples of this expression from B, C, $\cdots$, to get expressions free from x. These expressions will be of the form $B - b(aA)$, $C - c(aA)$, $\cdots$.

Now we suppose $B - b(aA)$ contains y with non-zero coefficient. The coefficient can be made equal to 1 by multiplying by a suitable constant d. Thus

$$dB - dbaA = y + \cdots.$$

We now subtract e times the expression above from $C - caA$; we choose e so that y does not appear in the result. We get the expression $C - caA - e(dB - dbaA)$.

Thus it is this expression that we suppose to be zero. It will be seen that the coefficient of C is 1. Hence

$$C - caA - e(dB - dbaA) = 0$$

is a non-trivial equation, which shows that C can be expressed in the form $fA + gB$; that is, C is a mixture of the preceding vectors A, B and does not contribute anything new to the space generated.

This proves our contention for the case where the zero vector appears at the third step. There is only verbal difficulty in describing the proof for the general case. Essentially it is the same as the proof above.

Question: If a zero vector appears first at the fourth stage, show that D is a mixture of A, B, C.

I shall leave it to you to satisfy yourself that such a proof can be constructed for the appearance of a zero vector at any stage of the process, and shall regard ourselves as having established the following.

THEOREM. *If a zero vector appears at the m-th stage in the reduction of P_1, P_2, P_3, $\cdots$, then P_m is a mixture of P_1, P_2, $\cdots$, P_{m-1}.*

On pages 145–146 we discussed, from a geometrical viewpoint, various ways of finding a basis for a plane. Always there seemed to be two vectors in such a basis, and it seems plausible that if we choose *any* two vectors in a plane, not in the same direction and neither being zero, then these two vectors generate the whole plane. That is, it seems that in 2 dimensions any 2 linearly independent vectors generate the whole space. In the same way, by considering geometrical space of 3 dimensions, it seems reasonable that any 3 independent vectors generate the whole space. (See page 166 for the geometrical significance of linear dependence.) We are led to conjecture the following theorem.

THEOREM. *In space of n dimensions, any n linearly independent vectors generate the whole space.*

It may help to see how this is proved if we consider a particular example. Linear expressions of the form $ax + by + cz + dt$ constitute a space of 4 dimensions. Suppose we have 4 expressions of this type, which are known to be linearly independent. Then by mixing these 4 expressions, it should be possible to obtain any expression of the form $ax + by + cz + dt$.

Our 4 expressions can be reduced to standard form. The expressions are linearly independent; no one of them can be a mixture of the preceding ones; hence, by the theorem of page 179, it is impossible for a zero vector to appear in the reduction. (For if a zero vector did appear, it would prove that one of the original vectors was a mixture of the others.) Accordingly, the reduction must go to its full length. There must be 4 vectors in the standard form.

But there is only one way of getting 4 vectors in the standard form, namely by means of the following pattern.

$$
\begin{aligned}
A &= x + ey + fz + gt, \\
B &= \phantom{x + {}} y + hz + kt, \\
C &= \phantom{x + ey + {}} z + mt, \\
D &= \phantom{x + ey + fz + {}} t.
\end{aligned}
$$

We cannot possibly have a pattern like those on page 172, in which long steps appear, and several letters $x, y, z, \cdots$, drop out between one line and the next. For if we did have this, we would have used up all our letters x, y, z, t before we reached the fourth expression, D. Only by the utmost economy, dropping one letter only at each line, can we reach four lines. (We are compelled to drop one letter at each stage. The definition of standard form requires it. See the explanation on page 173.)

Thus the standard form A, B, C, D must be of the type shown above. (There is, of course, nothing to prevent some or all of the numbers e, f, g, h, k, m being zero.)

But now we can clearly obtain any expression $ax + by + cz + dt$ by a suitable mixture of A, B, C, D. By taking aA, we obtain the correct coefficient for x. By adding a suitable multiple of B to aA, we can make the coefficient of y correct, without altering the coefficient of x. This would in fact give us $aA + (b - ae)B$, but the details of the calculation are not helpful. By adding a suitable multiple of C, we make the coefficient of z correct, without disturbing the coefficients of x and y. Finally, by adding a suitable multiple of D, we obtain the correct coefficient for t.

This mode of approach generalizes immediately to n linear expressions in n variables x_1, x_2, $\cdots$, x_n. The stages in the argument are the following.

(i) The n expressions being independent, the standard form must contain n expressions.

(ii) A standard form with n expressions in it must have the form

$$
\begin{aligned}
A_1 &= x_1 + \cdots \cdots \cdots \\
A_2 &= \quad\;\; x_2 + \cdots \cdots \cdots \\
A_3 &= \qquad\quad\;\; x_3 + \cdots \cdots \\
&\;\cdots \cdots \cdots \cdots \cdots \\
A_n &= \qquad\qquad\qquad\qquad x_n
\end{aligned}
$$

(iii) Any linear expression $a_1x_1 + a_2x_2 + \cdots + a_nx_n$ can be gotten by taking suitable values c_1, c_2, $\cdots$, c_n in $c_1A_1 + c_2A_2 + \cdots + c_nA_n$.

Anyone who has understood the procedure for $n = 4$ will see that no new idea is needed to prove the general case.

One final objection has to be met. We have taken a particular example of a vector space, namely, linear expressions. But the theorem may be needed for some other example of a vector space—say, for a geometrical space. However, the first few pages of chapter 8 pointed out that work with vectors was essentially the same as work with linear expressions.

There are two ways of presenting the proof outlined above in a form that shows it to be quite general.

1. In a vector space of n dimensions, every vector is expressible as $a_1P_1 + a_2P_2 + \cdots + a_nP_n$. (See (V.10) on page 161, and the explanation of $P_1, P_2, \cdots,$ on page 160.) But this is a linear expression in $P_1, P_2, \cdots, P_n$. We simply rewrite our earlier proof. Whenever x_1 occurs we write P_1 instead. For x_2 we write P_2, and so on.

2. Alternatively, we may use the label $(a_1, a_2, \cdots, a_n)$ for a vector in space of n dimensions, as on page 152. The standard form, for 4 dimensions say, will then appear as

$$A = (1, e, f, g),$$
$$B = (0, 1, h, k),$$
$$C = (0, 0, 1, m),$$
$$D = (0, 0, 0, 1).$$

The argument that any vector (a, b, c, d) can be expressed as a mixture of A, B, C, D follows essentially the same lines. aA has the first number inside the bracket correct. By bringing in B, we can make the second number correct also. And so on. The whole proof can be carried through in this notation.

The somewhat informal discussion we have just had contains all the ideas needed for the proof of the theorem. If you understand these ideas, you can verify that the theorem is established. You can, if you like, write out a formal proof. I do not give a formal proof in full, since it would not be needed by anyone who has understood these ideas, and would be meaningless to anyone who has not.

We now have our final theorem of this chapter.

THEOREM.   *Any $(n + 1)$ vectors in a vector space of n dimensions are linearly dependent.*

Proof.   Let the vectors be $V_1, V_2, \cdots, V_n, V_{n+1}$. It may be that $V_1, V_2, \cdots, V_n$ are linearly dependent, being connected by a relation $c_1V_1 + c_2V_2 + \cdots + c_nV_n = 0$, where $c_1, \cdots, c_n$ are not all zero. If so, we have

$$c_1V_1 + c_2V_2 + \cdots + c_nV_n + 0 \cdot V_{n+1} = 0.$$

Since $c_1, \cdots, c_n$ are not all zero, the coefficients in this last equation are not all zero; that is, $V_1, \cdots, V_{n+1}$ are linearly dependent.

So the theorem holds if $V_1, \cdots, V_n$ are linearly dependent.

Suppose then that $V_1, \cdots, V_n$ are linearly independent. Then, by the preceding theorem, any vector in the space can be expressed as mixture of $V_1, \cdots, V_n$. Hence V_{n+1} can be expressed as a mixture of $V_1, \cdots, V_n$. Hence $V_1, \cdots, V_{n+1}$ are linearly dependent.

Thus the theorem holds in either case, and is proved.

On page 170 we proved that n linearly independent vectors generated a space of n dimensions. Why then, it might be asked, did we find it necessary to prove on pages 180–182 that, in a space of n dimensions, any n linearly independent vectors generated the whole space? Is it not obvious that they generate the whole space? For instance, someone might say, "take the case $n = 2$. We have a plane; we take any two independent vectors; they generate a plane—isn't it obvious that this plane must be the plane we started with?" It is indeed plausible that it should be so. However, the chain of reasoning just given assumes a certain result, namely that one plane cannot be contained in another plane—this to be understood in the sense that you cannot remove certain points from a plane, and still have a complete plane remaining. More generally, if S and T are spaces of n dimensions, and T is contained in S, then T is identical with S. If one n-dimensional space lies in a second n-dimensional space, then it completely fills it.

Now this result sounds very reasonable, but we have to prove it. And, in effect, that is what we did on pages 180–182.

On page 148 the question was raised whether a space might be at one and the same time a space of n dimensions and a space of $(n + 1)$ dimensions. It seemed unlikely, but again unlikely things do happen—for instance, there is a curve that completely fills a square; it is as well to have a proof. The last theorem of this chapter supplies the proof. In space of $(n + 1)$ dimensions there are $n + 1$ independent vectors—for example the vectors

$$V_1 = (1, 0, 0, \cdots, 0),$$
$$V_2 = (0, 1, 0, \cdots, 0),$$
$$V_3 = (0, 0, 1, \cdots, 0),$$
$$\cdot \quad \cdot \quad \cdot \quad \cdot \quad \cdot \quad \cdot \quad \cdot \quad \cdot$$
$$V_{n+1} = (0, 0, 0, \cdots, 1).$$

In space of n dimensions there cannot exist $(n + 1)$ independent vectors. Hence it is impossible for a space of n dimensions to be a space of $(n + 1)$ dimensions.

Chapter 10

Fields Regarded as Vector Spaces

WE HAVE NOW proved some results for vector spaces, but it is far from evident that these results will tell us anything interesting about fields. In fact, some very useful theorems about fields can be obtained.

To see how this happens, we review the procedure of modern mathematics. The underlying idea of modern mathematics is to extract the essence of any proof, and separate it from purely accidental aspects. In this way generality is obtained.

If you want to write a paper in modern algebra, you look at a theorem somebody else has proved, and you see just what he has used to prove it. For example, the theorem that any quadratic has at most two roots was originally proved for numbers. We examine the proof and ask, "What properties of numbers does it use?" We find that it uses only the properties of numbers expressed by axioms (1) through (12). This means that the proof can be written in such a way that it applies to any set of elements—not necessarily numbers—that obey axioms (1) through (12).

So, without having used any real originality, we can state a more general theorem: "In any structure, the elements of which obey axioms (1) through (12), a quadratic has at most two roots."

We can now shorten this statement by bringing in a technical term, "field." Any structure, we say, for which axioms (1) through (12) hold, will be referred to as a field. Our theorem then takes the form, "In any field a quadratic has at most two roots."

A most important point should be noticed here; the misunderstanding of it frequently causes confusion. The qualification for being a field is positive, not negative. That is to say, to be a field, a structure must satisfy axioms (1) through (12). *It is not disqualified from being a field because it obeys other axioms in addition to (1) through (12).*

There is an obvious reason for taking it this way. The proof that a quadratic equation has at most two roots uses axioms (1) through (12) only: so it applies to any structure for which these axioms hold. The proof nowhere requires that the structure does not satisfy other axioms. Real numbers, for instance, do satisfy other axioms. There is the relation $a < b$, "a less than b," which is defined, and for which a system of axioms holds; for example, it is an axiom that if $a < b$ and $b < c$, then $a < c$. Not all fields permit such a relation to be defined; you would, for instance, find difficulty in defining an order relation for the arithmetic modulo 5; again, we do not use the symbol $<$ for complex numbers. However, the symbol $<$ does not occur anywhere in the proof that a quadratic has at most two roots. For the proof of this theorem, it is entirely irrelevant whether the structure has a relation $a < b$ or not.

Thus, it is correct to say, "The axioms for a field do not require $a < b$ to be defined." It would be incorrect to say, "No structure in which $a < b$ is defined is a field." In the same way the definition of "human" does not require the possession of unusual physical strength,

American citizenship, or the wearing of a hat. But a strong, American, hat-wearing individual is still to be regarded as human; and all theorems that can be deduced from the axioms specifying humanity will be true for such an individual. We do not think of "a human being," "a strong creature," "an American," "a hat wearer" as being distinct objects. Rather these terms emphasize different aspects of objects—or, it may well be, different aspects of one single individual.

Thus, there is no contradiction between our having proved, in exercise 7 on page 31, that the numbers $a + b\sqrt{2}$ (with a, b rational) form a field, and on page 154 that they form a vector space of 2 dimensions over the rationals. The usual objection is, "You can multiply $a + b\sqrt{2}$ and $c + d\sqrt{2}$, but you cannot multiply two vectors."

The mistake here is again that of using the tests negatively rather than positively. The basic property of a vector space of 2 dimensions is that every element of it is a mixture of two basic ingredients only. Now every number $a + b\sqrt{2}$ is a mixture of 1 and $\sqrt{2}$. By using this property (in the form of the more precise statements we had earlier), we can prove for the numbers $a + b\sqrt{2}$ all the theorems appropriate to spaces of 2 dimensions.

The fact that $\sqrt{2}$ can be multiplied by $\sqrt{2}$ corresponds to the aspect of this structure as a field. We cannot deal with this aspect by means of the vector axioms.

The useful fact is that $a + b\sqrt{2}$ is simultaneously a vector space and a field. We can prove for it both the theorems appropriate to vector spaces and to fields. In this way we may be led to new results, obtained by combining these theorems.

In terms of our earlier illustration, we suppose it a theorem that human beings are conscious of what is happening, and that a hat-wearer's head is warm. We can deduce that a human being wearing a hat is conscious of warmth in the head. This result unites the two theories: it cannot be proved in either theory alone. A human being may have a cold head in the absence of a hat. A lower animal, although wearing a hat and hence having a warm head, may not be conscious of the warmth.

There is a property of the numbers $a + b\sqrt{2}$ that will serve to illustrate this theme, and lead us to a more general result.

Every number of the form $a + b\sqrt{2}$ satisfies an equation, with rational coefficients, which is quadratic (or simpler in particular cases). For if

$$x = a + b\sqrt{2},$$
$$x - a = b\sqrt{2},$$
$$(x - a)^2 = 2b^2.$$

Hence $x^2 - 2ax + a^2 - 2b^2 = 0$.

This is an equation with rational coefficients.

This method works all right in this particular case, but it does not generalize easily. For instance, it is true that every number $a + b\sqrt[3]{2} + c\sqrt[3]{4}$ satisfies a cubic equation over the rationals, and that every number $a + b\sqrt{2} + c\sqrt{3} + d\sqrt{6}$ satisfies an equation of the fourth degree over the rationals; a, b, c, d of course represent rational numbers. One can easily construct more and more complicated examples of such theorems. The simple method used above for $a + b\sqrt{2}$ does not enable us to see the truth of these more complicated theorems. We accordingly look for a method that will generalize.

We return, then, to proving that $a + b\sqrt{2}$ satisfies a quadratic and look for a more illuminating proof.

A quadratic expression $px^2 + qx + r$ may be written

$p \cdot x^2 + q \cdot x + r \cdot 1$; that is to say, it is a mixture of x^2, x, and 1. We want to show that, for some rational numbers p, q, r, this mixture will be zero. Let us take a particular case, say $x = 3 + 5\sqrt{2}$. What are x^2, x, and 1?

$$1 = 1,$$
$$x = 3 + 5\sqrt{2},$$
$$x^2 = 59 + 30\sqrt{2}.$$

We seek to make a mixture of these three things zero. Now, from the equations above,

$$px^2 + qx + r = (59p + 3q + r) + (30p + 5q)\sqrt{2}.$$

As $59p + 3q + r$ and $30p + 5q$ are rational if p, q, r are rational, we can only make the above mixture of 1 and $\sqrt{2}$ zero by making

$$59p + 3q + r = 0 \qquad (1)$$
$$30p + 5q \quad\;\; = 0 \qquad (2)$$

Here we have two equations in the three unknowns p, q, r. Our theorem will be proved if we can show (i) that non-trivial solutions exist, (ii) that some such solution makes p, q, r rational. The trivial solution $p = q = r = 0$ of course is useless.

In this particular case, we can solve the equations, and verify that the solution is rational. However, we are seeking to extract some general principle.

The language of vector spaces helps us to do this. $px^2 + qx + r \cdot 1 = 0$ with rational p, q, r is another way of saying that x^2, x, 1 are linearly dependent over K, the rationals.

Now, if 1, $\sqrt{2}$ are chosen as a basis, x^2 has the label $(59, 30)$; x has the label $(3, 5)$; 1 the label $(1, 0)$.

Equations (1) and (2) can be combined in the vector equation

$$p(59, 30) + q(3, 5) + r(1, 0) = (0, 0).$$

But we know that any 3 vectors in 2 dimensions are linearly dependent. So we can be sure that numbers p, q, r, not all zero, exist which satisfy the above equation.

We need these p, q, r to be *rational*. Can we be sure of fulfilling this condition? We are working in the framework of Example 4 on page 154. K is the field of rational numbers. The numbers a, b that appear in any label (a, b) are rational. The linear dependence of vectors A, B, C means that $pA + qB + rC = 0$ with p, q, r *elements of K*, not all zero. All the work proceeds within the field K. It may help you to see this, if we work through the proof that $(n + 1)$ vectors in n dimensions are linearly dependent, applying its procedure to the particular case we have here, namely that the three vectors

$$A = (1, 0),$$
$$B = (3, 5),$$
$$C = (59, 30),$$

in 2 dimensions are linearly dependent. We should first express A and B in standard form; this gives us two vectors which form a basis for the whole space. Hence C is expressible as a mixture of these. In fact,

$$B - 3A = (0, 5).$$
$$\therefore D = \tfrac{1}{5}B - \tfrac{3}{5}A = (0, 1).$$

A and D make the standard form. Evidently

$$C = 59A + 30D,$$
$$= 59A + 30(\tfrac{1}{5}B - \tfrac{3}{5}A),$$
$$= 41A + 6B.$$

The numbers 1, 0, 3, 5, 59, 30 that occur in the labels for A, B, C are necessarily rational. In the calculation, we start with these numbers and perform addition, subtraction, multiplication, and division, *but no other operation is used*. Accordingly, we stay always within K, the field of rationals. We are bound to arrive at a rational solution p, q, r.

In this particular case, $C - 6B - 41A = 0$: so $p = 1$, $q = -6$, $r = -41$, and $x = 3 + 5\sqrt{2}$ satisfies $x^2 - 6x - 41 = 0$. This, of course, is the same equation that we should have obtained by applying our first method. For this particular case, the second method is longer. Its value lies in the fact that it applies to other cases. The purpose of the method, too, is not so much to calculate the equation, as to show that an equation exists.

The work above shows that the theorem "Any $(n + 1)$ vectors in n dimensions are linearly dependent" can be stated in elementary algebra. For suppose the vectors are

$$V_1 \text{ with label} \quad (a_1, b_1, c_1, \cdots, g_1),$$
$$V_2 \text{ with label} \quad (a_2, b_2, c_2, \cdots, g_2),$$
$$V_{n+1} \text{ with label} \quad (a_{n+1}, b_{n+1}, c_{n+1}, \cdots, g_{n+1}),$$

where all the numbers $a_1, \cdots, g_{n+1}$ belong to a field K. The linear dependence of these $(n + 1)$ vectors means that there are numbers $p_1, p_2, \cdots, p_{n+1}$, belonging to K and not all zero such that $p_1 V_1 + p_2 V_2 + p_{n+1} V_{n+1} = 0$. That is,

$$a_1 p_1 + a_2 p_2 + \cdots + a_{n+1} p_{n+1} = 0,$$
$$b_1 p_1 + b_2 p_2 + \cdots + b_{n+1} p_{n+1} = 0,$$
$$\cdot \quad \cdot \quad \cdot \quad \cdot \quad \cdot \quad \cdot \quad \cdot \quad \cdot \quad \cdot$$
$$g_1 p_1 + g_2 p_2 + \cdots + g_{n+1} p_{n+1} = 0,$$

so we have the theorem. *If n equations in $(n + 1)$ unknowns, of the type shown above, have all their coefficients lying in a field K, then these equations have a solution $p_1, p_2, \cdots, p_{n+1}$ composed of elements of the field K, not all zero.*

It is essential to include the words "of the type shown above." For instance, the three equations in four unknowns

$$x + y + z + r = 1,$$
$$x + 2y + 3z + 4r = 2,$$
$$3x + 7y + 12z + 17r = 3,$$

have no solution, as is easily verified if you regard r a
known, and try to solve for x, y, z. But these equation
are not of the type specified, since they have non-zer
constant terms 1, 2, 3.

This example also shows that the theorem is not trivial
Having fewer equations than unknowns does not alway
guarantee the existence of a solution.

We now use the method developed above to show tha
$x = a + b\sqrt[3]{2} + c\sqrt[3]{4}$, ($a$, b, c rational), satisfies an equa
tion $px^3 + qx^2 + rx + s = 0$, where p, q, r, s are no
all zero.

We noted on page 121 that the numbers $t + u\sqrt[3]{2} +$
$v\sqrt[3]{4}$, with t, u, v rational, form a field. Since x belong
to this field, x^2 and x^3 also belong to the field, by fiel
axiom (2). We could work out x^2 and x^3 in terms of a, b, c
but this work would be wasted. All that matters for the
latter part of the proof is that x^2 and x^3 are of the form
$t + u\sqrt[3]{2} + v\sqrt[3]{4}$. Accordingly, we write

$$1 = 1,$$
$$x = a + b\sqrt[3]{2} + c\sqrt[3]{4},$$
$$x^2 = d + e\sqrt[3]{2} + f\sqrt[3]{4},$$
$$x^3 = g + h\sqrt[3]{2} + k\sqrt[3]{4},$$

where d, e, f, g, h, k could be expressed in terms of a, b, c,
but all we really need to know is that these symbols
represent rational numbers.

We could now consider $px^3 + qx^2 + rx + s$ and show
that it would be zero if the four quantities p, q, r, s satisfied the three equations

$$pg + qd + ra + s = 0,$$
$$ph + qe + rb = 0,$$
$$pk + qf + rc = 0.$$

We know that three such equations in four unknowns always have a rational solution. Hence we know that there are rational numbers p, q, r, s, not all zero, for which $px^3 + qx^2 + rx + s = 0$, and our theorem is proved.

In order to explain this proof, I have had to bring in symbols d, e, f, g, h, k. But really I have not made any calculations with these symbols. If I wanted to prove that $a + b\sqrt[5]{2} + c\sqrt[5]{4} + d\sqrt[5]{8} + e\sqrt[5]{16}$ (a, b, c, d, e rational) always satisfies an equation of the fifth degree over the rationals, I should pretty well use up the whole alphabet in explaining the proof. But the proof would not contain any new idea. It is therefore natural to coin a name for such a situation, to have a brief way of indicating that this proof works. That name we already have: "vector space."

Our proof that every number $a + b\sqrt[3]{2} + c\sqrt[3]{4}$ satisfies a cubic equation can now be stated very briefly. The rational numbers being denoted by K, the totality of numbers $t + u\sqrt[3]{2} + v\sqrt[3]{4}$, with t, u, v rational, constitutes the field $K(\sqrt[3]{2})$.

We now argue let $x = a + b\sqrt[3]{2} + c\sqrt[3]{4}$. x is an element of $K(\sqrt[3]{2})$. Since $K(\sqrt[3]{2})$ is a field, x^2 and x^3 are also elements of $K(\sqrt[3]{2})$. 1 is an element of $K(\sqrt[3]{2})$.

Hence 1, x, x^2, x^3 are elements of $K(\sqrt[3]{2})$.

But every element of $K(\sqrt[3]{2})$ is a mixture of 1, $\sqrt[3]{2}$, $\sqrt[3]{4}$, with rational coefficients. Hence $K(\sqrt[3]{2})$ is a vector space of 3 dimensions* over K. Hence any four elements of it are linearly dependent over K. Hence, for rational

---

* 1, $\sqrt[3]{2}$, $\sqrt[3]{4}$ form a basis since they are linearly independent over K. But we do not even need to prove this. If they were linearly dependent, $K(\sqrt[3]{2})$ would be a space of *less than* 3 dimensions, and the proof would be even stronger than it is now.

numbers p, q, r, s, not all zero, we have $px^3 + qx^2 +$
$rx + s = 0$.   Q.E.D

Question 1:   If w stands for the real number such that
$w^7 = 2$ and $s = a + bw + cw^2 + dw^3 + ew^4 + fw^5 + gw^6$
where a, b, c, d, e, f, g are rational numbers, prove that
s satisfies an equation of the seventh degree with rational
coefficients. (This question is intended to show the economy of thought and statement made possible by using
the vector terminology, as compared with the notation
of elementary algebra.)

Question 2:   Do the elements $a + b\sqrt{2} + c\sqrt{3} + d\sqrt{6}$
form a vector space over the rational numbers K? (a, b,
c, d rational numbers). Of what dimension? What is the
degree of the equation with rational coefficients satisfied
by the general element of this correction?

Question 3:   Let $m = \sqrt{2} + \sqrt{3}$. Calculate m^2 and m^3.
Do 1, m, m^2, m^3 form a basis for the space considered in
question 2? What is the simplest equation over the rationals that is satisfied by m? What are the other roots of
this equation? (The equation for m can be found quite
easily by elementary algebra.)

Question 4:   An irrational number r satisfies an equation $f(x) = 0$, which is of degree n and irreducible over
the rational numbers K. Find a basis for $K(r)$, regarded
as a vector space over K. Of how many dimensions is it?
What is the degree of the equation with rational coefficients satisfied by an arbitrary element of $K(r)$?

In our examples, we have taken K as the field of rationals. Often indeed, we are interested in knowing
whether an element satisfies an equation with rational
coefficients. But we might also be interested to know
whether it satisfied an equation with roots drawn from
some other field, F.

We have the following general theorem. *Suppose F is any field, and G is a field that contains F. Suppose G is a vector space* n *dimensions over F; that is to say, there are fixed elements* b_1, b_2, $\cdots$, b_n *of G such that every element of G can be represented in the form* $a_1b_1 + a_2b_2 + \cdots + a_nb_n$ *by choosing suitable elements* a_1, a_2, $\cdots$, a_n *of F. Then every element of G satisfies an equation of degree n (or less) over F.*

For instance, if R denotes the field of the rationals, F might be $R(\sqrt{2})$ and G might be $F(\sqrt{3})$. That is, we start with the rationals, R. F is obtained by bringing in the new element $\sqrt{2}$; anything that can be gotten by adding, subtracting, multiplying, and dividing with rational numbers and $\sqrt{2}$ belongs to F. In fact, every element of F can be expressed in the form $p + q\sqrt{2}$, with rational p, q. We use the letters u, v to denote elements of F.

G is obtained from F by allowing the free use of the extra symbol $\sqrt{3}$. In fact, every element of G can be put in the form $u + v\sqrt{3}$, where u, v belong to F.

Thus, in this example, $b_1 = 1$ and $b_2 = \sqrt{3}$ are the fixed elements of G. $a_1 = u$ and $a_2 = v$ are variables, representing elements of F. Thus G is a vector space of 2 dimensions over F, and every element of G satisfies an equation of the second degree—that is, a quadratic—with coefficients in F.

For example, $x = \sqrt{2} + \sqrt{3}$ is an element of G, with $= \sqrt{2}$ and $a_2 = 1$.

Evidently $(x - \sqrt{2})^2 = 3$, which simplifies to

$$x^2 - 2\sqrt{2}\,x - 1 = 0.$$

This is a quadratic equation over F. The coefficients re 1, $- 2\sqrt{2}$, $- 1$, all cf which lie in F. It is not a quadratic over the rationals R, since $-2\sqrt{2}$ is not in

If we wish to obtain the equation over R satisfied I
$\sqrt{2} + \sqrt{3}$, we write the quadratic above in the for

$$x^2 - 1 = 2\sqrt{2}\, x.$$

Squaring gives

$$(x^2 - 1)^2 = 8x^2,$$

whence

$$x^4 - 10x^2 + 1 = 0.$$

This equation is of the fourth degree, which is qui
consistent with our theorem. For in $u + v\sqrt{3}$, the gener
element of G, the quantities u and v are elements of
that is to say, we may write

$$u = c + d\sqrt{2},$$
$$v = h + k\sqrt{2},$$

where c, d, h, k are rational.

Thus, the general element of G is

$$(c + d\sqrt{2}) + (h + k\sqrt{2})\,\sqrt{3}$$

or

$$c + d\sqrt{2} + h\sqrt{3} + k\sqrt{6}.$$

G is thus a vector space of 4 dimensions over R, wit
1, $\sqrt{2}$, $\sqrt{3}$, $\sqrt{6}$ as a basis. Accordingly, any element
G must satisfy an equation of the fourth degree at mos
with rational coefficients. Thus,

G is a vector space of 2 dimensions over F.

G is a vector space of 4 dimensions over R.

Any element of G satisfies a quadratic equation
coefficients from F are allowed, but an equation of th
fourth degree is all we can guarantee if only ration
coefficients are allowed.

Finding the Equation of Lowest Degree for Any Element

We have already met the principle that x satisfying an equation of degree n over any field K is the same as , x, x^2, $\cdots$, x^n being linearly dependent over K. (See pages 189–194.)

Thus, if x satisfies an equation of degree n, but no equation of degree less than n, then 1, x, x^2, $\cdots$, x^n will be linearly dependent, but 1, x, x^2, $\cdots$, x^{n-1} will be linearly independent.

Thus, it is possible to find the value of n by forming the quantities 1, x, x^2, x^3, $\cdots$, and seeing at what point linear dependence first happens. The standard form for vectors gives a systematic way of doing this. The appearance of a zero vector is the signal for linear dependence having arisen.

Example. Find the degree of the simplest equation over the rationals satisfied by $x = \sqrt{2} + \sqrt{3}$.

It saves rearrangements if we take our basis in the order 1, $\sqrt{2}$, $\sqrt{6}$, $\sqrt{3}$ so that (a, b, c, d) is the label for $a + b\sqrt{2} + c\sqrt{6} + d\sqrt{3}$.

$$
\begin{array}{ll}
1 & \text{has label } (1, 0, 0, 0), \\
x = \sqrt{2} + \sqrt{3} & \text{has label } (0, 1, 0, 1), \\
x^2 = 5 + 2\sqrt{6} & \text{has label } (5, 0, 2, 0), \\
x^3 = 11\sqrt{2} + 9\sqrt{3} & \text{has label } (0, 11, 0, 9), \\
x^4 = 49 + 20\sqrt{6} & \text{has label } (49, 0, 20, 0).
\end{array}
$$

There is no point in calculating further. We now have five vectors in 4 dimensions. These must be linearly dependent; but, conceivably, linear dependence might have arisen even before x^4 was reached.

The vectors of the standard form are

$$1 \qquad \text{with label } (1, 0, 0, 0),$$
$$x \qquad \text{with label } (0, 1, 0, 1),$$
$$\tfrac{1}{2}(x^2 - 5) \qquad \text{with label } (0, 0, 1, 0),$$
$$-\tfrac{1}{2}(x^3 - 11x) \qquad \text{with label } (0, 0, 0, 1).$$

No zero vector has appeared, so 1, x, x^2, x^3 are inde
pendent and generate the whole space. x^4 is 49 times the
first vector added to 20 times the third vector of the
standard form above. That is,

$$x^4 = 49 \cdot 1 + 20 \cdot \tfrac{1}{2}(x^2 - 5),$$

whence $x^4 - 10x^2 + 1 = 0$ as we expected from our
earlier work. We have now demonstrated, by using a
vector procedure, that x does not satisfy any simple
equation over the rationals.

This type of example is included here not so much be
cause we wish to perform calculations of this kind, bu
so that you can become used to thinking of elements of
fields as vectors. This idea is important for the genera
theory.

Question: Find the degree of the simplest equation
over the rationals satisfied by $\sqrt{3} - \sqrt{2}$. Also find the
equation.

Must a Field Have a Dimension
Over a Sub-field?

Often one field G contains another field F. (Then F
is called a sub-field of G. Thus the rationals are a sub
field of the reals because the reals contain the rationals.
We have had examples in which G was a vector space of
n dimensions over F. Must this always happen? If a field
G contains a sub-field F, must G be a vector space of
dimensions over F?

We must first get one difficulty out of the way. Sup

ose, for example, that G is the real numbers and F the ationals. Now the numbers $\sqrt{2}$, $\sqrt{3}$, $\sqrt{5}$, $\sqrt{7}$, $\cdots$, the quare roots of the prime numbers, are all real numbers, ence in G. But they are linearly independent over the ationals (this can be proved; you should find it reasonable that, for example, $\sqrt{11}$ cannot be expressed as a ational mixture of $\sqrt{2}$, $\sqrt{3}$, $\sqrt{5}$, and $\sqrt{7}$). Thus G contains as many elements as you like that are linearly independent over F. Now a space of n dimensions cannot contain $(n + 1)$ independent elements. So G cannot have any finite dimension over F, in this case.

Accordingly, in any theorem we obtain, we must include some condition to rule out the possibility that G contains infinitely many elements independent over F.

Is there anything left to investigate? Will not our theorem have to run, "If G is of finite dimensions over F, then G is of n dimensions over F for some integer n," which is futile? No, there is still a possibility to consider. For instance, is it possible for G to be something more than a space of 2 dimensions over F, but less than a space of 3 dimensions?

What would this mean? Let small letters, a_0, a_1, a_2, $\cdots$, denote elements of F, while capital letters P_1, P_2, $\cdots$, denote elements of G. "G is something more than a space of two dimensions over F." This means that, if we take the two ingredients 1, P_1, all possible mixtures $a_0 \cdot 1 + a_1 \cdot P_1$ give elements of G, but these do not completely cover G. There are some elements of G that cannot be represented in this way. It is of course assumed that 1, P_1 are linearly independent over F. On the other hand, G is something "less than a space of 3 dimensions over F." This means that taking three elements 1, P_1, P_2 would give us too much. The elements $a_0 \cdot 1 + a_1 \cdot P_1 + a_2 \cdot P_2$ give all the elements of G, and some others besides.

The question is, is such a state of affairs possible? In fact it is not possible. We can prove that if G is more than a space of 2 dimensions over F, then it is at least a space of 3 dimensions over F.

We have 1, P_1 linearly independent over F, and $a_0 \cdot 1 + a_1 \cdot P_1$ always gives an element of G. But some element of G cannot be expressed in this form. Choose any such element; call it P_2.

First result. 1, P_1, P_2 are linearly independent over F. For, if not, there are elements of F, c_0, c_1, c_2, not all zero, such that $c_0 \cdot 1 + c_1 \cdot P_1 + c_2 \cdot P_2 = 0$. If $c_2 \neq 0$, we can divide by c_2 and solve for P_2. This gives P_2 as a mixture of 1 and P_1. But we supposed P_2 outside the elements of the form $a_0 \cdot 1 + a_1 \cdot P_1$. So $c_2 = 0$. But this means that 1, P_1 are linearly dependent with $c_0 \cdot 1 + c_1 \cdot P_1 = 0$. And this also is ruled out. Accordingly, it is impossible that 1, P_1, P_2 should be linearly dependent over F; our result is proved.

This shows that 1, P_1, P_2 generate a space of 3 dimensions. They do not lie in any space of 2 dimensions (for no 2 dimensional space can contain 3 independent vectors).

Thus the elements $a_0 \cdot 1 + a_1 \cdot P_1 + a_2 \cdot P_2$ do form a space of 3 dimensions. We proceed to show that this space lies completely inside G.

Second result. Every element of the form $a_0 \cdot 1 + a_1 \cdot P_1 + a_2 \cdot P_2$ belongs to G.

Proof. By our assumptions, $a_0 \cdot 1 + a_1 \cdot P_1$ is an element of G for all a_0, a_1 of F. P_2 is an element of G (see how it was defined just before the statement of "*first result*"). a_2 is an element of F; since F is contained in G, then a_2 belongs to G. Thus, $a_0 \cdot 1 + a_1 \cdot P_1$, a_2, P_2 are three elements of G. Addition and multiplication of elements of a field always give elements of that field. But $a_0 \cdot 1 + a_1 \cdot P_1 + a_2 \cdot P_2$ is obtained from the three elements of G

just listed by multiplication and addition only. Hence, this expression is an element of G, as had to be proved.

Thus G certainly contains a space of 3 dimensions over F.

The above proof does not use any properties peculiar to the numbers 2 and 3. We can show, without using any new idea, that a field never lies between one whole number and the next in its dimension over a sub-field.

Question: The field G contains the field F. G contains a vector space of n dimensions over F, but these are elements of G not belonging to this vector space. Prove that G contains a vector space of $(n + 1)$ dimensions over F.

It is now easy to see how things work out. A field G contains a sub-field F, that is, every element of F is in G.

It may be that G coincides with F. If so, G is a space of 1 dimension over F, with 1 as a basis.

But there may be an element P_1 in G but not in F. Then G certainly contains the vector space of 2 dimensions over F, with basis 1, P_1. This space may fill G. Then G has 2 dimensions over F.

If it does not fill F, there is an element P_2 of G outside it. G then contains the 3-dimensional space with basis 1, P_1, P_2. If this space fills G, then G is of 3 dimensions over F. If not, we bring in P_3.

So we continue. How can the process end? Well, first of all, it may not end. We may be able to go on forever bringing in new elements.

This is case (i); for every n, we can find 1, P_1, P_2, $\cdots$, P_{n-1}, n elements of G linearly independent over F.

On the other hand, the process may come to an end. We obtain, for some n, a space contained in G with basis 1, P_1, P_2, $\cdots$, P_{n-1}, but we are unable to make the next step. What can be preventing us? All that we need for the next step is some element not in the space generated by the basis 1, P_1, P_2, $\cdots$, P_{n-1}. Our inability to proceed can only mean that there is no such element. That is, the field G coincides with the space; thus G is a space of n dimensions over F. This is case (ii). We thus have the following theorem.

THEOREM.   *If F is a sub-field of G, either (i) there is no limit to the number of elements of G linearly independent over F, or (ii) G is exactly a vector space of n dimensions over F, where n is some natural number.*

EXERCISES

1. If R is the rationals, $F = R(\sqrt{6})$, $G = R(\sqrt{2}, \sqrt{3})$, show that F is a sub-field of G, and find the dimension of G over F.

2. It is known that π does not satisfy any equation with rational coefficients. If $F = R$, the rationals, and $G = R(\pi)$, does case (i) or case (ii) of the above theorem apply?

3. Find the dimension of $R(\sqrt[6]{2})$ over $R(\sqrt{2})$, R being the rationals.

4. Find the dimension of $R(\sqrt{1 + \sqrt{5}})$ over $R(\sqrt{5})$.

5. Find the dimension of $R(\sqrt{1 + \sqrt[3]{2}})$ over $R(\sqrt[3]{2})$.

6. Find the dimension of $GF(2^2)$ over $GF(2)$, and of $GF(2^3)$ over $GF(2)$. (See page 130 for terminology.)

Repeated Extensions of a Field

We have already had examples in which a field is repeatedly extended. For example, by adjoining $\sqrt{2}$ to the rationals R, we obtain $S = R(\sqrt{2})$. By adjoining $\sqrt[3]{5}$ to S, we obtain $T = S(\sqrt[3]{5}) = R(\sqrt{2}, \sqrt[3]{5})$. T contains 1, $\sqrt[3]{5}$, $\sqrt[3]{25}$. It also contains 1, $\sqrt{2}$. It must contain the products of these elements, which we can arrange naturally in a rectangle.

$$\begin{array}{cc}
1 & \sqrt{2} \\
\sqrt[3]{5} & \sqrt{2}\cdot\sqrt[3]{5} \\
\sqrt[3]{25} & \sqrt{2}\cdot\sqrt[3]{25}
\end{array}$$

These six quantities are linearly independent over R, nd any element of T is a mixture of these with rational oefficients. Thus T is of 6 dimensions over R. S is of 2 dimensions over R.

The arrangement of the 6 quantities in a rectangle emphasizes that 6 is 3 times 2. It suggests that such an rrangement would be possible in any extension of S; hat the basic quantities could always be written

$$\begin{array}{cc}
1 & \sqrt{2} \\
A & A\sqrt{2} \\
B & B\sqrt{2} \\
\cdot \quad \cdot \quad \cdot & \cdot \quad \cdot \quad \cdot \\
M & M\sqrt{2}
\end{array}$$

There would thus be an even number of elements in he basis. This suggests the theorem: "Any extension of $R(\sqrt{2})$ has dimension $2n$ over R, for some integer n."

It is easy to verify that you cannot have an extension f $R(\sqrt{2})$ of 3 dimensions over R. For suppose you could. Let 1, $\sqrt{2}$, Q be a basis of such a field. 1, $\sqrt{2}$, Q must be linearly independent over R; otherwise they will not form a basis for a space of 3 dimensions. The product $Q\sqrt{2}$ must be in this field. Hence, it must be a mixture of , $\sqrt{2}$, Q. That is, for some rational a, b, c,

$$Q\sqrt{2} = a + b\sqrt{2} + cQ.$$

Hence

$$Q(\sqrt{2} - c) = a + b\sqrt{2}.$$

Now $\sqrt{2} - c$ is not zero, for c is rational while $\sqrt{2}$ is irrational. Hence, we can divide by $\sqrt{2} - c$ Both

$\sqrt{2} - c$ and $a + b\sqrt{2}$ lie in the field $R(\sqrt{2})$. Hencϵ their quotient also lies in this field. Thus, for some ra tional d, e

$$Q = d + e\sqrt{2}.$$

But this shows Q to be a mixture of 1, $\sqrt{2}$, which contrϵ dicts our assumption that 1, $\sqrt{2}$, Q are linearly indϵ pendent.

The position is this. You cannot get *a field* by intro ducing *one* new element Q into the basis. Either Q is mixture of 1, $\sqrt{2}$, which adds nothing new, and you sti have a space of 2 dimensions over R; or Q and $Q\sqrt{2}$ bot make a contribution and you have a space of 4 dimen sions with the basis

$$\begin{array}{cc} 1 & \sqrt{2} \\ Q & Q\sqrt{2} \end{array}$$

You can of course have a field of 3 dimensions over I $1, \sqrt[3]{2}, \sqrt[3]{4}$ is the basis of such a field. But this field, $R(\sqrt[3]{2}$ does not contain $\sqrt{2}$. So it is not an extension of $R(\sqrt{2}$

There is nothing special about square roots in th connection. $R(\sqrt[3]{2})$ has dimension 3 over R. Any exter sion of $R(\sqrt[3]{2})$ will have dimension $3n$ over R. For ir stance, $R(\sqrt[3]{2}, \sqrt[5]{3})$ has the basis

$$\begin{array}{ccc} 1 & \sqrt[3]{2} & \sqrt[3]{4} \\ \sqrt[5]{3} & \sqrt[5]{3} \cdot \sqrt[3]{2} & \sqrt[5]{3} \cdot \sqrt[3]{4} \\ \sqrt[5]{9} & \sqrt[5]{9} \cdot \sqrt[3]{2} & \sqrt[5]{9} \cdot \sqrt[3]{4} \\ \sqrt[5]{27} & \sqrt[5]{27} \cdot \sqrt[3]{2} & \sqrt[5]{27} \cdot \sqrt[3]{4} \\ \sqrt[5]{81} & \sqrt[5]{81} \cdot \sqrt[3]{2} & \sqrt[5]{81} \cdot \sqrt[3]{4} \end{array}$$

and forms a space of 15 dimensions over R. 15 is a mu tiple of 3.

We may now state the theorem of which the abov

have been examples. It is convenient to use the abbreviation $P \subset Q$ for "P is contained in Q," that is, every element of P is an element of Q. (P may coincide with Q, but usually will be a part, not the whole, of Q.)

THEOREM. *Let F, G, H be fields, $F \subset G \subset H$. Let G be a vector space of p dimensions over F, and H a vector space of q dimensions over G. Then H is a vector space of $p \cdot q$ dimensions over F.*

In the first example of this section, $F = R$, $G = S$, $H = T$, $p = 2$, $q = 3$, and T is of $2 \cdot 3 = 6$ dimensions over R.

The proof of this theorem is extremely simple. It involves no calculations. It requires only an understanding of such ideas as linear dependence over a particular field. It may help you to follow the proof if you apply it to the particular examples we have had.

Proof. It will be convenient to use small letters, a, b, c, $\cdots$, for elements of F, and capitals A, B, C, $\cdots$, for elements of G. Capitals from the end of the alphabet will be used for elements of H, say U, V, W, $\cdots$.

We now start to express concretely the information at our disposal.

"H is a vector space of q dimensions over G." This means that every element of H is a mixture of q basic ingredients. The coefficients, which show how much of each ingredient is used, are drawn from G. But the ingredients themselves belong to H. (Look back to earlier examples. So far as the present statement is concerned, it is irrelevant that G contains a sub-field F. One could take as an example R for G and $R(\sqrt{2})$ for H. This example of course will not do for the later part of the work.)

Thus every element of H can be expressed in one and only one way as

$$V = A_1 U_1 + A_2 U_2 + \cdots + A_q U_q \tag{1}$$

where $U_1, \cdots, U_q$ are *fixed* elements of H, whil $A_1, \cdots, A_q$ are variables over G. The element $U_1, \cdots, U_q$, since they generate a space of q dimension are linearly independent over G. $V = 0$ only if $A_1 = A_2 = \cdots = A_q = 0$.

Now G in its turn is a vector space of p dimension over F. Every element of G can be expressed as

$$B = c_1 D_1 + c_2 D_2 + \cdots + c_p D_p \qquad (2$$

where $D_1, \cdots, D_p$ are fixed elements of G, linearly in dependent over F, and $c_1, \cdots, c_p$ are variables over F

Now $A_1, \cdots, A_q$ are elements of G, and hence each them can be expressed as a mixture of $D_1, \cdots, D_p$ wit coefficients from F. Suppose, then, that

$$\begin{aligned}
A_1 &= c_{11} D_1 + c_{12} D_2 + \cdots + c_{1p} D_p \\
A_2 &= c_{21} D_1 + c_{22} D_2 + \cdots + c_{2p} D_p \\
&\cdot \quad \cdot \quad \cdot \quad \cdot \quad \cdot \quad \cdot \quad \cdot \quad \cdot \quad \cdot \quad \cdot \quad \cdot \\
A_q &= c_{q1} D_1 + c_{q2} D_2 + \cdots + c_{qp} D_p.
\end{aligned} \qquad (3$$

If we substitute these values in the expression for V an multiply out, we find that

$$\begin{aligned}
V = \; & c_{11} U_1 D_1 + c_{12} U_1 D_2 + \cdots + c_{1p} U_1 D_p \\
& + c_{21} U_2 D_1 + c_{22} U_2 D_2 + \cdots + c_{2p} U_2 D_p \\
& + \cdot \quad \cdot \quad \cdot \quad \cdot \quad \cdot \quad \cdot \quad \cdot \quad \cdot \quad \cdot \quad \cdot \\
& + c_{q1} U_q D_1 + c_{q2} U_q D_2 + \cdots + c_{qp} U_q D_p.
\end{aligned} \qquad (4$$

We now have V expressed as a mixture of the pq fixe quantities $U_1 D_1, \cdots, U_q D_p$. The coefficients $c_{11}, \cdots, c_q$ are elements of F. V is any element of H. Thus H cer tainly cannot be a vector space of more than pq dimen sions. It will be a vector space of less than pq dimension if $U_1 D_1, \cdots, U_q D_p$ are linearly dependent over F. If w can show these to be linearly independent, we shal know that they generate a space of exactly pq dimensions

If they were linearly dependent, it would be possibl

to find $c_{11}, \cdots, c_{qp}$, not all zero, in such a way that V, in equation (4) would be zero.

But we have already seen, just below equation (1), that $V = 0$ only if $A_1 = A_2 = \cdots = A_q = 0$.

Further, $D_1, \cdots, D_p$ are linearly independent over F. In equations (3), $A_1 = 0$ only if $c_{11} = c_{12} = \cdots = c_{1p} = 0$; $A_2 = 0$ only if $c_{21} = c_{22} = \cdots = c_{2p} = 0$, and so on through $A_q = 0$ only if $c_{q1} = c_{q2} = \cdots = c_{qp} = 0$.

Thus $V = 0$ only when all of $c_{11}, \cdots, c_{qp}$ are zero. This means that $U_1 D_1, \cdots, U_q D_p$ are linearly independent. Accordingly, they generate a space of pq dimensions. We have shown that every element of H lies in this space.

We must also show that every element of the space lies in H. But all the quantities $c_{11}, \cdots, c_{qp}$; $U_1, \cdots, U_q$; $D_1, \cdots, D_p$ belong to H. In equation (4) they are combined by addition and multiplication only. Since H is a field, the result must lie in H. Thus, whatever values are chosen for $c_{11}, \cdots, c_{qp}$, the right-hand side of equation (4) gives an element of H.

Thus every element V has a label $(c_{11}, \cdots, c_{qp})$, and every such label belongs to some element V of H.

H is thus a vector space of pq dimensions over F. The theorem is proved.

Chapter 11

Trisection of an Angle

BEFORE going into details we examine, in broad outline, the proof that angles cannot be trisected. The meaning of the statement should first be clarified. There are plenty of mechanical devices for trisecting angles. Trisection is impossible only within the rules proposed by the ancient Greeks—compass and straightedge alone permitted as implements, and these to be used only in the ways customary in Euclidean geometry.

Certain angles, of course, can be trisected. The angles 30° and 15° can be constructed; so it is certainly possible to trisect 90° and 45°. But, in general, given an angle, there is no procedure for trisecting it.

If there were a procedure for trisecting angles, this procedure could be applied to the angle 60°. This would give us a construction for the angle 20°, since 60° itself is easily constructed. We shall prove *the impossibility of constructing the angle 20° by Euclidean means*. This is sufficient to show that no general procedure for trisecting angles can exist.

The attack on the problem is algebraic. We translate geometrical constructions into algebraic terms—as is done in analytical geometry. It will be shown that *any geometrical construction whatever* is algebraically equivalent to specifying a number with the help only of rational numbers and square root signs. For example, the number

$$c = \sqrt{2} + \sqrt{\tfrac{3}{4} + 5\sqrt{3}}$$

is specified by means of the rational numbers 2, $\tfrac{3}{4}$, 5, 3, and some square root signs. This number corresponds to a geometrical construction. It is easy to construct geometrically two lines whose lengths are in the ratio c.

If the angle 20° were constructible, it would be easy to draw lines having the ratio 2 cos 20°. Let w stand for the number 2 cos 20° for the remainder of this book. We shall show that w is the root of a cubic equation over the rationals, but not of any equation of lower degree. In fact, 1, w, w^2 are linearly independent over the rationals R; these numbers form a basis for $R(w)$, and $R(w)$ is of dimension 3 over R.

If it were possible to construct 20° geometrically, it would be possible to represent w by an expression something like the one that specifies c; that is, an expression built up by means of square roots and rational numbers alone.

And here we have the germ of a contradiction. Any number specified by square roots, it can be shown, lies in a field of dimension 2^n over R, where n is a whole, positive number. Call this field F.

Now we suppose w to lie in F. As F is a field, w^2 also must belong to F; thus 1, w, w^2 all belong to F, and any rational mixture of these also belongs to F. That is, $R(w)$ is contained in F. F must have a dimension over $R(w)$ (see page 202). It is easily seen that this dimension cannot be infinite. Call it q. Then the dimension of F over R is $3q$ (see page 205).

Thus the presence of an element such as w, associated with a cubic equation, always betrays itself. If a field F

contains w, then the dimension of F over R must be divisible by 3.

But any number specified by square roots lies in a field F of dimension 2^n over R, and 2^n is never divisible by 3.

Thus it is impossible for w to lie in any field of dimension 2^n over R; it is therefore impossible for w to be expressed by any collection of square roots and rational numbers. This means that the angle $20°$ cannot be constructed by any Euclidean procedure.

Three things, then, are required to fill out the details of this proof. (I) To show the correspondence between geometrical constructions and the repeated extraction of square roots. (II) To show that any number expressed by means of square roots lies in a field of dimension 2^n. (III) To show that w satisfies a cubic equation over the rationals R, but no simpler equation. We now consider these three in detail.

I. *Geometrical Constructions*

A certain amount of care is required to make sure that we do not overlook any possible type of geometrical construction. A construction might, for example, make use of a subsidiary construction; we might, say, construct a regular pentagon (which Euclid showed how to do) and then transfer an angle of $72°$ from this pentagon to some place in the main figure. There might be several such subsidiary constructions involved, and the figure might fall into several separate pieces. This is rather awkward for the argument we are using. However, we avoid this complication. If, as suggested above, we required an angle of $72°$, it would not matter where we constructed our regular pentagon, or how large its side was. Accordingly, we could construct it on a line already marked in our main figure. This might be most inconvenient from the draftsman's viewpoint; a very messy figure might result. Mathematically, it would make no difference at all. In this way, all the separate pieces of the figure could be joined into one connected figure. For the subsidiary constructions begin with some instruction such as, "Choose any two points" or "Draw any circle." (If the subsidiary constructions did not begin in this way, they would have to mention specific points or distances, and the only specific points and distances are those already on the main figure, or connected to it in some way.) We are thus free to choose any points or any circle we like; we elect to choose points already on the diagram, or to draw a circle determined by the existing figure.

In the same way, whenever an arbitrary element appears in a construction, we choose it to suit ourselves. For example, if A and B are known points, the perpendicular bisector of AB can be constructed by drawing a circle of arbitrary radius about A, and a circle of the same radius about B. The circles must of course be so chosen that they intersect. The particular radius used does not affect the result. So we are perfectly free to make the construction more definite: instead of an arbitrary, unknown radius, we select some suitable, known radius. In our example, we might use AB itself as radius.

How do we know that there would always be *some* known length suitable for an arbitrary radius? In outline, the argument is the following: a suitable circle is one that intersects a line or another circle; if the construction is possible at all, it means that some real number will do for the radius of the circle; if l is the length of some known line, we can construct lines of length $2l$, $3l$, $\frac{1}{2}l$, $\frac{1}{4}l$, and so on—in short, any rational multiple of l—and thus get as near to any real number as we like. A sufficiently small change in the radius of a circle will leave it still intersecting in the required manner.

Our argument will be in terms of analytical geometry. Suppose we set out in our attempt (foredoomed to failure) to construct an angle of 20°. In the course of our construction, we shall mark certain points. Let O and P be the first two points that arise in the construction. We take O as origin, and OP as unit distance along the x-axis. As the construction proceeds, we obtain points, lines, circles, all related in a definite manner to O and P. Our earlier agreement cuts out all arbitrary elements. If we have to choose "any point" or "any distance," we choose a point with rational coordinates, a distance that is a rational multiple of OP. Incidentally, Euclidean geometry allows us to construct the position of any point with rational coordinates; so we are not going outside Euclidean construction when we select any such point.

We are starting then with the points $(0, 0)$ and $(1, 0)$ marked. The permissible steps are:

(i) To draw a line joining two known points.

(ii) To mark the point where two known lines intersect.

(iii) To draw a circle with known center and known radius.

(iv) To mark the points where a line cuts a circle.

(v) To mark the points where circles intersect.

(vi) To place the compass points on two known points and then to move the compass without changing this distance.

All of these we want to consider in terms of analytic geometry. A point is specified by its coordinates (a, b). A line is specified by its equation $y = mx + c$, unless it happens to be perpendicular to OP, when it will have an equation $x = k$. A circle with center (a, b) and radius r has the equation $(x - a)^2 + (y - b)^2 = r^2$.

In item (iii) we speak of "a known radius." A radius is known when it is the distance between two points already determined. Item (vi) describes the operation performed when we are preparing to draw a circle with a prescribed radius. A radius, or a distance between two points, is of course specified by a single number, d.

As we carry out operations (i) through (vi) successively, we obtain new geometrical objects at each step. These new objects—points, lines, circles, distances—are determined by the old ones from which they arise. The numbers specifying the new objects are functions of the numbers that have arisen earlier in the process.

For example, suppose the figure, at some stage of construction, contains two lines with equations $y = m_1x + k_1$, and $y = m_2x + k_2$. We can determine their point of intersection (provided they are not parallel). It is easily verified that the coordinates of the intersection are rational functions of the numbers m_1, m_2, k_1, k_2.

In operation (vi), if we have two points (a_1, b_1) and (a_2, b_2) in the figure, we can stretch the compasses from one point to the other. The distance, d, that now exists between the points of the compasses, is given by

$$d = \sqrt{(a_1 - a_2)^2 + (b_1 - b_2)^2}$$

Question: Verify that, in each of the operations (i) through (vi), the new numbers introduced arise from the old ones by addition, subtraction, multiplication, division, and extraction of square root, and never involve any other operation.

Suppose now that any geometrical construction is given. As this construction is carried out, we keep a record of it in analytical form. Whenever a point is determined by the construction, we note down its coordinates (a, b). Whenever a line is drawn, we write down its equation, either in the form $y = mx + c$ or in the form $x = k$, whichever is appropriate. We record all the distances, d, between points on the figure. When a circle is drawn, we note its equation.

In this way, we arrive at a list of numbers. Some numbers arise as coordinates, some as distances, some as coefficients in equations (like m and c for instance). Each number is determined by numbers that occur earlier in the list. The earliest numbers in the list are rational numbers, 0 and 1. The only operations used in making the list are the rational operations—addition, subtraction, multiplication, division—and the extraction of square roots.

Thus, regardless of the way by which it enters into the geometrical construction, every number we meet is of the type stated earlier—formed with the help of rational numbers and square root operations alone. Statement (I) is thus justified.

II. *Fields of Dimension* 2^n

We now wish to show that every number in our list belongs to a field of dimension 2^n over R, the rationals.

Consider an example first of all. Suppose we construct, as is easy to do, the four points $(0, 0)$, $(1, 0)$, $(1, 1)$, $(1, 2)$. The lines $y = 0$, $x = 1$, $y = x$, $y = 2x$ join these points. The six distances between the four points are 1, 1, 1, 2, $\sqrt{2}$, $\sqrt{5}$. (Circles must have been used to construct the right angle in the figure. In this example, we ignore these, to avoid complications.)

The first numbers appearing above are rational; the last two, $\sqrt{2}$ and $\sqrt{5}$, are irrationals.

Up to a certain stage, the numbers are included in R, the field of the rationals. When $\sqrt{2}$ appears,

we have to extend the field to $R(\sqrt{2})$, and when $\sqrt{5}$
also appears, we have to make a further extension
to $R(\sqrt{2}, \sqrt{5})$. $R(\sqrt{2})$ is of dimension 2 over R
(basis, 1, $\sqrt{2}$); $R(\sqrt{2}, \sqrt{5})$ is of dimension 4 over R.
The dimensions 2 and 4 are both powers of 2. This
example illustrates the result we are hoping to prove.

All the numbers listed for the construction above
lie in the field $R(\sqrt{2}, \sqrt{5})$. We arrived at the field
$R(\sqrt{2}, \sqrt{5})$ simply by adjoining to R all the irrational
numbers in our list. We could, if we wished, adjoin the
rational numbers on the list too, but that of course would
make no difference, as they are already in R.

It looks as though we have a great variety of cases to
consider, for in other constructions we may meet not
only expressions like $\sqrt{2}$ and $\sqrt{5}$, but more complicated
expressions like $\sqrt{3 + 4\sqrt{5}}$. However, we do not need
to get entangled in these complications. There is essentially one situation that recurs again and again.

Remember that we list the numbers in an order corresponding to the order of geometrical construction.
Each number is determined by the earlier numbers. We
start with the rationals, R. As each new irrational number occurs in the list, we adjoin it to the field. At each
stage of the process, we thus have a field, which contains
all the numbers in the list up to a certain point. Let F
stand for the field obtained by adjoining to R the first
m numbers on the list. Let h be the $(m + 1)$-th number
on the list. h is determined by the earlier numbers on the
list; it can be expressed by a formula containing them,
and this formula contains at most *a single square root sign;*
no other irrational operation is involved.

It may be that the formula giving h does not contain
the square root symbol at all [for example, operations
(i) and (ii)].

Again, it may be that there is a square root operation in the formula, but that the numerical values allow this square root to be extracted without introducing any new irrationals. For example, the distance between two points involves a square root; but if the points happen to be the origin and the point $(3, 4)$, the distance is given by the rational number 5, and no new irrational comes in. The same effect can occur with irrational expressions; the expression $\sqrt{59 + 30\sqrt{2}}$ makes no difference if it is adjoined to $R(\sqrt{2})$, for $59 + 30\sqrt{2}$ is the square of a quantity in $R(\sqrt{2})$, namely, $3 + 5\sqrt{2}$.

Here, then, is one possibility; the $(m + 1)$-th number, h, may lie in the field F that contains the first m numbers. Then no action is called for, and we would pass on to consider the number after h in the list.

The other possibility is that h is not in the field F. In this case, it must be of the form $s + t\sqrt{u}$, where s, t, u all belong to F; s, t, u stand for rational functions of the earlier numbers in the list; the earlier numbers all belong to F, and F is a field; that is why s, t, u must belong to F.

Accordingly, adjoining h to F is the same as adjoining $\sqrt{u}$ to F. u, of course, is not the square of an element of F. $F(\sqrt{u})$ is thus the field obtained by adjoining the first $(m + 1)$ numbers of the list to R. Suppose F has dimension p over R. Since $F(\sqrt{u})$ has dimension 2 over F, the dimension of F over R must be $2p$ (see chapter 10).

Thus, at any such step, when we adjoin a number on the list, the dimension of our field is either *unchanged* or *doubled*. Since we start with the rational field, R, which is of dimension 1 over itself, we necessarily end up with a power of 2 as the dimension. This justifies statement (II).

III. *The Cubic for w*

The formula $\cos 3\theta = 4 \cos^3 \theta - 3 \cos \theta$ is a standard result in trigonometry. If we take the angle 20° for θ and write $x = \cos 20°$, since $\cos 60° = 1/2$, we have $4x^3 - 3x = 1/2$. This may be written $8x^3 - 6x - 1 = 0$, or $(2x)^3 - 3(2x) - 1 = 0$. This suggests bringing in a new symbol for $2x$, and in fact w, defined earlier in this chapter as $2 \cos 20°$, is just that; $w = 2x$. Substitution gives the equation $w^3 - 3w - 1 = 0$.

So w satisfies a cubic with rational coefficients. w^3 is accordingly a rational mixture of 1 and w, and every power of w is a mixture of 1, w, w^2. It looks as if $R(w)$ is of dimension 3 over R, with 1, w, w^2 as the basis. Now this is in fact true, but unfortunately we cannot go straight to that conclusion. The reason why can be explained either in the language of vector spaces or of equations. We saw in chapter 10 that these were closely connected; we showed that a certain quantity satisfied an equation by considering its powers and proving them linearly dependent.

The fact that w satisfies a cubic equation means that 1, w, w^2, w^3 are linearly dependent. But it may be that already 1, w, w^2 are linearly dependent; if so, $R(w)$ will be of dimension 2 in general. It may even happen that 1, w are linearly dependent; if so, w is rational and $R(w)$ is the same as R; then $R(w)$ has dimension 1.

Thus the fact that w satisfies a cubic equation proves $R(w)$ to be of dimension 3 *or less*. If $R(w)$ is of dimension 2, then w satisfies a quadratic equation with rational coefficients (see chapter 10). If $R(w)$ is of dimension 1, then w satisfies a linear equation with rational coefficients.

In terms of equations, it is easy to see how a quantity

can satisfy a cubic equation and also an equation of lower degree. For example, the cubic equation $7t^3 + 6t - 13 = 0$ holds for the rational number $t = 1$. The cubic equation $s^3 + s^2 - 2s - 2 = 0$ holds for the irrational quantity $s = \sqrt{2}$. This cubic is simply $(s + 1)(s^2 - 2) = 0$.

In both our examples, the cubic factors. We complete our proof by showing (i) that w could only satisfy an equation of lower degree if the cubic factored, and (ii) that the cubic $x^3 - 3x - 1$ does not factor into polynomials with rational coefficients.

The proof of (i) follows a fairly natural train of thought. Let us take an example where a quantity satisfies two equations. There is an irrational number z that satisfies the two equations

$$z^4 + 2z^3 + z^2 - 1 = 0, \qquad \text{(I)}$$
$$z^3 + 3z^2 + z - 2 = 0. \qquad \text{(II)}$$

But from these two equations, we can derive yet another equation satisfied by z. If we subtract z times (II) from (I), we shall obtain an equation not containing any z^4 term, namely,

$$-z^3 + 2z - 1 = 0. \qquad \text{(III)}$$

We now have two cubics, (II) and (III), satisfied by z. From these we can obtain an equation in which z^3 does not appear. In this particular example, we have simply to add (II) and (III). This gives

$$3z^2 + 3z - 3 = 0$$

or, on dividing by 3,

$$z^2 + z - 1 = 0. \qquad \text{(IV)}$$

But when is this going to stop? We have now reached a quadratic; if we subtract z times (IV) from (II), we shall obtain a quadratic, and by combining this with (IV), we should expect to obtain a linear equation for z. Actually, this does not happen. If we subtract z times (IV) from (II), we obtain $2z^2 + 2z - 2 = 0$. Dividing this by 2, we obtain equation (IV) again. Equation (IV) is the simplest equation with rational coefficients satisfied by z.

In effect, we have done a kind of long division above. Combining the steps, equation (IV) results on subtracting $(z - 1)$ times (II) from (I). In the language of division, when $z^4 + 2z^3 + z^2 - 1$ is divided by $z^3 + 3z^2 + z - 2$, the quotient is $z - 1$ and the remainder is $z^2 + z - 1$. We are not particularly interested in the quotient. It is the remainder that turns up in equation (IV). The reason why the process cannot be carried any further is that $z^2 + z - 1$ divides exactly into the polynomials that occur in equations (I) and (II). It is in fact their H.C.F. You have probably noticed that the calculations above are those we should do to obtain the H.C.F. of polynomials (I) and (II) by the method of chapter 4.

The object of these considerations is to show that H.C.F. comes quite naturally into the picture. The work above suggests that if a quantity z is a root of the equation $f(x) = 0$ and $g(x) = 0$, then it is also a root of the equation $h(x) = 0$, where $h(x)$ is the H.C.F. of $f(z)$ and $g(z)$.

It should not be hard to prove this, because we have only a few theorems about H.C.F. (The fewer theorems there are, the more quickly one can look through them and decide which are relevant. This may sound a paradox, but it is not.) The statements (i), (ii), (iii) of page 88 pretty well sum up what we know about H.C.F. Statement (ii) is the one that will help us. The form of it, appropriate to polynomials, is the following; if $h(x)$ is the H.C.F. of $f(x)$ and $g(x)$, then there exist polynomials $a(x)$, $b(x)$ such that

$$h(x) = a(x)f(x) + b(x)g(x). \qquad (V)$$

The desired result follows immediately. z is a root of $f(x) = 0$; this means $f(z) = 0$. z is a root of $g(x) = 0$; so $g(z) = 0$. Substitute z for x in equation (V). The right-hand side clearly becomes zero, as each term contains a zero factor. Hence $h(z) = 0$. This is what we wanted to show; z is a root of the polynomial $h(x)$.

Equation (V) also shows that the common factor $h(x)$ cannot be a trivial one. For example, if $f(x)$ were $x^3 - 1$ and $g(x)$ were $x^2 + 1$, the H.C.F. $h(x)$ would simply be 1. The two polynomials have only a trivial common factor if that factor is constant. *But this cannot happen in the situation that interests us.* For suppose it did. Then $h(x)$ is 1 and equation (V) becomes

$$1 = a(x)f(x) + b(x)g(x).$$

We suppose that $f(x)$ and $g(x)$ have the common root z. Substitute z for x. The right-hand side becomes zero, and we have $1 = 0$. But this is impossible.

Accordingly, if two polynomials with rational coefficients, $f(x)$ and $g(x)$, have a common *irrational* root z, this quantity is also a root of their H.C.F., $h(x)$; and $h(x)$ is not trivial, not constant, but a genuine, healthy polynomial. $h(x)$ can be calculated by the H.C.F. process, so that $h(x)$ also is a polynomial with *rational* coefficients.

Now we come to apply this to our quantity w. We know that w is a root of the polynomial $x^3 - 3x - 1$. We choose this polynomial for $f(x)$. We are investigating whether w can satisfy also a quadratic or linear equation. If w is the root of a linear or quadratic polynomial, call that polynomial $g(x)$. Then, by the argument above,

there is a polynomial $h(x)$ that is a factor both of $f(x)$
and $g(x)$, and this $h(x)$ is not just a constant. Since $h(x)$
is a factor of $g(x)$, the polynomial $h(x)$ is either linear or
quadratic—for $g(x)$ is supposed quadratic at most. Since
$h(x)$ is a factor of $f(x)$, it follows that $f(x)$ can be split
into rational factors. All of this, of course, is on the
assumption that w satisfies some equation of the first
or second degree—an assumption we are trying to dis-
prove by showing that it leads to a contradiction.

We have now established our contention (i); if w
satisfies any equation simpler than the cubic, then the
cubic factors.

We finally establish the contradiction by proving
assertion (ii); the cubic cannot be factored into polynomials with rational coefficients.

This proof is quite long enough already, and we shall
shorten this final stage by quoting a standard theorem
without proof. The line of argument followed is one
that—in a loose form—would occur to any competent
high school student of algebra.

Suppose a student is asked to find out whether
$2x^2 + x + 3$ can be factored. The student will consider
the possibility of such factors as $x + 1$, $x + 3$, $2x + 1$,
$2x + 3$, perhaps also $x - 1$, $x - 3$, $2x - 1$, $2x - 3$.
That is, he considers whole number coefficients only,
and these he chooses in a special way. He only considers
for the constant term whole numbers that are factors
of 3, and for the coefficient of x he only considers factors of 2. He does not consider the possibility, say
$(\frac{5}{2}x + \frac{6}{7})(\frac{4}{5}x + \frac{7}{2})$. In so doing, he is right (though he
does not know why he is right). It was proved by Gauss
that, if we have a polynomial with *whole number* coefficients, and we cannot factor it by means of polynomials
with whole number coefficients, then we cannot factor
it by bringing in fractions either. If such a polynomial

does not factor with the help of whole numbers, then it is irreducible over the rationals.

Now it is very easy to see that $x^3 - 3x - 1$ cannot be factored into polynomials with whole number coefficients. If it could be factored as $(ax + b)(cx^2 + dx + e)$, we should have $ac = 1$ and $be = -1$. That is, a would be a factor of 1 and b a factor of -1. This restricts a and b to the values 1 and -1, if a and b are whole numbers. Thus $x + 1$ and $x - 1$ are the only possible factors. It is easily seen that neither of these works. Thus the cubic cannot be factored with whole number coefficients; by Gauss' result, it cannot be factored into polynomials with rational coefficients. Assertion (ii) is now justified. We have gone round plugging one leak after another, and we hope the argument is by now reasonably watertight.

The Gauss theorem that we have quoted can be proved by an elementary proof of an essentially arithmetical nature. The argument we have given shows how modern algebraic concepts—fields, vector spaces, and their dimensions—can be used to prove theorems about elementary geometry and algebra.

Answers to Exercises

(PAGES 15–16)

1. Yes; the classes $a + b$ and ab are determined.

+	O	I	II		×	O	I	II
O	O	I	II		O	O	O	O
I	I	II	O		I	O	I	II
II	II	O	I		II	O	II	I

(1) through (7) do apply.

2. Again, the classes are determined. (1) through (7) apply.

+	O	I	II	III	IV
O	O	I	II	III	IV
I	I	II	III	IV	O
II	II	III	IV	O	I
III	III	IV	O	I	II
IV	IV	O	I	II	III

×	O	I	II	III	IV
O	O	O	O	O	O
I	O	I	II	III	IV
II	O	II	IV	I	III
III	O	III	I	IV	II
IV	O	IV	III	II	I

3. The tables for 7, 11, 13 ⋯ resemble those found in questions 2 and 3. But for 4, 6, 8, 9, 10, 12 ⋯ the multiplication tables differ from those in question 2 and 3. For instance, with the number 6, we have the II times table

$$\text{II} \cdot \text{ O} = \text{O}, \quad \text{II} \cdot \text{ I} = \text{II}, \quad \text{II} \cdot \text{II} = \text{IV},$$
$$\text{II} \cdot \text{III} = \text{O}, \quad \text{II} \cdot \text{IV} = \text{II}, \quad \text{II} \cdot \text{ V} = \text{IV}.$$

The products O, II, IV each occur twice. But in questions 2 and 3, in each multiplication table every symbol occurs once only. 3, 5, 7, 11, 13 are prime numbers. 4, 6, 8, 9, 10, 12 can be factored. This is the reason for the difference.

4.

	0	2	4	6	8			0	2	4	6	8
0	0	2	4	6	8		0	0	0	0	0	0
2	2	4	6	8	0		2	0	4	8	2	6
+ 4	4	6	8	0	2	× 4	4	0	8	6	4	2
6	6	8	0	2	4		6	0	2	4	6	8
8	8	0	2	4	6		8	0	6	2	8	4

(1) through (7) do apply.

Are these tables isomorphic with those in question 2? The addition tables suggest that we let O correspond to 0, I to 2, II to 4, III to 6, IV to 8. But this does not work with the multiplication table. I · I = I would correspond to 2 · 2 = 2, which is *not* so. We are tempted to leap to the conclusion that the systems are not isomorphic. But such a conclusion is only justified if we can show that there is no way of establishing a correspondence. We have only tried one way so far. We try again. Consider property (7). In the system above, which element plays the role of I? That is, which one makes no difference when you multiply by it? Answer, 6. Try I corresponding to 6. Then II = I + I would have to correspond to 6 + 6 = 2. III = II + I would correspond to 2 + 6 = 8, and IV = III + I to 8 + 6 = 4. O corresponds to 0. You can now check that any result in question II, "translated" by this scheme, gives a correct result in the 0, 2, 4, 6, 8 tables. The systems are isomorphic.

5.

II · II = IV	II · II · II = III	II · II · II · II = I
III · III = IV	III · III · III = II	III · III · III · III = I
IV · IV = I	IV · IV · IV = IV	IV · IV · IV · IV = I

One can of course calculate higher powers than these. The answers form a repeating pattern.

6. Subtraction is possible in all the arithmetics considered in questions 1 through 3. For the arithmetics corresponding to prime numbers, division with a unique answer exists (division by 0 excluded, of course). In the non-prime cases, one either gets no answer or several answers. Thus, in the arithmetic arising from 6, $II \cdot x = III$ has no solution, but $II \cdot x = IV$ has two solutions, $x = II$ and $x = V$.

7. The perfect squares are O, I, IV. No number is prime. Even I has factors $I = II \cdot III = IV \cdot IV$. The arithmetic has no need of negative numbers and fractions. Subtraction and division can always be carried out, without introducing any new symbols.

(PAGE 20)

Each symbol occurs exactly once in each row of the addition tables.

(PAGES 24–25)

1. Number	Square	Cube	Fourth Power
0	0	0	0
1	1	1	1
2	4	3	1
3	4	2	1
4	1	4	1

(Compare question 5, page 16.)

By inspection of the tables above, $x^2 = 1$ for $x = 1$ and $x = 4$; $x^3 = 1$ only for $x = 1$; $x^4 = 1$ for $x = 1, 2, 3, 4$.

2. As in ordinary algebra, we find

$$(x + y) \cdot (x + y) \cdot (x + y) = x^3 + 3x^2y + 3xy^2 + y^3.$$

As $3 + 3 = 1$, modulo 5, the next multiplication by $x + y$ gives

$$(x + y) \cdot (x + y) \cdot (x + y) \cdot (x + y)$$
$$= x^4 + 4x^3y + x^2y^2 + 4xy^3 + y^4.$$

The final multiplication, since $4 + 1 = 0$ modulo 5, gives

$$(x + y) \cdot (x + y) \cdot (x + y) \cdot (x + y) \cdot (x + y) = x^5 + y^5.$$

Many points for discussion arise from this question. Can you have a 5th power when working modulo 5, since only the numbers 0, 1, 2, 3, 4 are admitted? See page 57.

3. $(x^2 + 1)/(x + 2) = x + 3$ modulo 5. This answer may also be written $x - 2$. $x^2 + 1 = 0$ for $x = 2, 3$.

4. $x^2 + x + 3 = (x + 2)(x + 4)$.

5. (i) 1, 2; (ii) 1, 1; (iii) 2, 2; (iv) 1, 4.
   (i) $(x - 1)(x - 2)$; (ii) $(x - 1)^2$; (iii) $(x - 2)^2$;
   (iv) $(x - 1)(x - 4)$.

6. Quotient $x^2 + 4x + 1$, remainder 1.

7. Yes.

8. Yes. $x = 1$ is a solution.

9. Values are 2, 0, 0, 2, 0, 0. The equation has *four* roots, 1, 2, 4, 5.

10. (i) All except (*10*) and (*12*).
    (ii) All except (*10*) and (*12*).

11. (i) Clearly not. Question 9 gives an example where a quadratic has four roots, although—see question 10 (i)—statements (*7*) through (*9*) and (*11*) hold.

   (ii) Yes. The quadratic with roots a, b is $(x - a)(x - b) = 0$. If a third root c, different from a and b existed, we should have $(c - a) \cdot (c - b) = 0$. Now use statement (*12*).

12. (i) Yes. $x^2 + 2$ for example.
    (ii) Yes. $x^2 + 2$ for example.

13. It has no other solution. (Compare question 1.) $(x^3 - 2)/(x - 3) = x^2 + 3x + 4$. This quadratic has no factors. If it had, we should be able to find further solutions of $x^3 - 2 = 0$.

(PAGE 31)

1. All but (*8*), (*10*), (*11*).
2. All but (*10*), (*11*).
3. All tests passed, a field.
4. A field.

5. A field.
6. All but (10).
7. Field.
8. Passes (1), (3), (5), (8), (9) only. Perhaps (11).
9. All but (10).
10. Field.
11. Field.
12. Field.
13. All but (10), (12).

(PAGES 31–32)

Question for investigation. This question is answered in chapter 3.

(PAGE 36)

Modulo 3, $x(x - 1)(x - 2) = x^3 - x$.
Modulo 5, $x(x - 1)(x - 2)(x - 3)(x - 4) = x^5 - x$.

(PAGE 70)

1. When the polynomial $f(x)$ is divided by the polynomial $x - a$, let the quotient be the polynomial $q(x)$ and the remainder the constant polynomial R. Then

$$f(x) = (x - a) \cdot q(x) + R \cdots \text{(I)}. \quad x \text{ indeterminate.}$$

By the theorems in chapter 2, if, in equation I, the indeterminate x is replaced by any fixed element of F, we obtain a true statement. Suppose the indeterminate x is replaced by the fixed element a. We then have

$$f(a) = 0 \cdot q(a) + R \cdots \text{(II)}.$$

Equation II is a statement about fixed elements of F.
Now $0 \cdot q(a) = 0$ and $0 + R = R$.
Hence $f(a) = R \cdots \text{(III)}$.
This is the remainder theorem. Note that R is used in two senses. In equations II, III, it stands for a particular element of

F; in equation I it denotes the constant polynomial, corresponding to that element.

2. By saying that the polynomial $ax^2 + bx + c$ has at mo two roots, we mean that it is impossible to find three distinc elements k, m, n of F such that

$$ak^2 + bk + c = 0 \cdots \text{(I)}$$
$$am^2 + bm + c = 0 \cdots \text{(II)}$$
$$an^2 + bn + c = 0 \cdots \text{(III)}$$

We assume that a is not zero.

Suppose that the three equations above were satisfied. Wit the help of the remainder theorem, equation I shows that th remainder would be zero if $ax^2 + bx + c$ were divided b $x - k$. That is, $x - k$ is a factor of $ax^2 + bx + c$. Similarly from equation II, $x - m$ is a factor of $ax^2 + bx + c$.

Hence $ax^2 + bx + c = a(x - k)(x - m)$. In this equatior x is an indeterminate. By the statement of chapter 2, a tru statement results if x is replaced everywhere by the fixed ele ment n.

Hence $an^2 + bn + c = a(n - k)(n - m)$.

Using equation III, $0 = a(n - k)(n - m)$.

You can now show that this contradicts field axiom (12) For we have assumed $a \neq 0$. $n - k \neq 0$ and $n - m \neq 0$ sinc n, k, m were supposed distinct.

(PAGE 80)

In question 1, a solution is given. Others exist.

1 (*i*). $x = -3$, $y = 2$.

1 (*ii*). $x = 5$, $y = -3$.

1 (*iii*). $x = 5$, $y = -7$.

2. No. For all integers x, y, the expression $4x + 6y$ give an even number; it can never give the odd number 1.

3. k must be divisible by h, the H.C.F. of a and b.

(PAGE 81)

1. $7x + 17y = 1$ has a solution $x = 5$, $y = -2$. S $7 \cdot 5 - 17 \cdot 2 = 1$. Hence $7 \cdot 5 = 1$ modulo 17. So 5 is th reciprocal of 7.

As $3 \cdot 11 - 2 \cdot 17 = -1$, the reciprocal of 11 is -3, which equals 14 modulo 17.

2. 6 and 241.

3. $2/7 = 5$, $5/6 = 10$.

(PAGE 84)

Question for discussion. No. They satisfy the same axioms, but it is not possible to establish a correspondence between the elements, such as is required for isomorphism. The integer 1 and the constant polynomial 1 must correspond. To preserve the addition tables, the integer $2 = 1 + 1$ must correspond to the polynomial 2; repeating the argument, the integer n must correspond to the constant polynomial n, for every positive n. It is easily seen that this must hold also for negative n. Now we have used up all the integers, and have none left to put into correspondence with x, x^2, etc.

(PAGES 86–89)

Exercises left to reader.

(PAGES 106–107)

1. If $x^2 + 1$ had a factor $x - a$, by the remainder theorem $a^2 + 1$ would be zero. Try $a = 0, 1, 2$ in turn. The theory can be constructed.

2. $x^2 + 3$ irreducible by argument similar to that in question 1. $x^2 + 1 = (x - 2)(x - 3)$, so reducible.

Procedure (ii) gives us complex numbers modulo 5.

Procedure (i) may be interpreted in two ways. If we regard $a + b\sqrt{-1}$ as giving 25 distinct elements, we find for example $(2 + \sqrt{-1}) \cdot (2 - \sqrt{-1}) = 0$ and axiom (12) fails. On the other hand, if we extract the square root, and write say $\sqrt{-1} = 2$ modulo 5, we merely obtain the arithmetic modulo 5 again, described in a wasteful manner. In this sense, we obtain a field, but not a new one.

3. $x \cdot x = x^2; x(x+1) = x^2 + x; (x+1)(x+1) = x^2 + 1$
The quadratic $x^2 + x + 1$ does not appear in this list. It
irreducible, and is the only irreducible quadratic.

4.

	O	I	M	M +
O	O	O	O	O
I	O	I	M	M +
M	O	M	M + I	I
M + I	O	M + I	I	M

5.

	O	I	M	M +
O	O	O	O	O
I	O	I	M	M +
M	O	M	I	M +
M + I	O	M + I	M + I	O

Axioms (10) and (12) fail.

6. Yes.

7. $(2 + 3Q) \cdot (4 + 5Q) = 8 + 22Q$.

No. For example, $Q \cdot Q = 0$, so axiom (12) fails. The divisio
$1/Q$ is impossible, so axiom (10) fails.

8. $f(x) = (a - bx)/(a^2 + b^2)$.

$$k = b^2/(a^2 + b^2).$$

From $f(x)$, we obtain the reciprocal

$$(a - bJ)/(a^2 + b^2).$$

9. Nothing new, just the reals again. The graphs intersec
on the y-axis.

10. $x(x-1)(x-M)(x-M-1) = x^4 - x$. So $x^4 = x$ i
the required equation.

(PAGE 121)

Addition, subtraction, and multiplication give no difficulty. T
establish division, we show that each element, except zero, ha
a reciprocal. In fact, $(r\sqrt[3]{4} + s\sqrt[3]{2} + t)(a\sqrt[3]{4} + b\sqrt[3]{2} + c) =$
if $a = (s^2 - rt)/k$, and $b = (2r^2 - st)/k$, and $c = (t^2 - 2rs)/$
where $k = 4r^3 + 2s^3 + t^3 - 6rst$. (We ought to show tha

k is never zero for rational r, s, t. To do this requires a rather expert knowledge of elementary algebra. One might make use of the well-known factoring $x^3 + y^3 + z^3 - 3xyz = \frac{1}{2}\{x + y + z\}\{(x - y)^2 + (y - z)^2 + (z - x)^2\}$ and put $x = r\sqrt[3]{4}, y = s\sqrt[3]{2}, z = t$. It is a merit of modern algebra that it avoids this troublesome detail.)

The reciprocal of $\sqrt[3]{4} + 2\sqrt[3]{2} + 3$ is $(\sqrt[3]{4} - 4\sqrt[3]{2} + 5)/11$.

(PAGE 129)

1. $n = 7$.
2. All the non-zero elements except 1 have this property.
3. Q, Q^2, Q^4 are all roots.
4. Q^3, Q^5, Q^6 are roots of $x^3 + x^2 + 1 = 0$. By the remainder theorem, $x^3 + x^2 + 1 = (x - Q^3)(x - Q^5)(x - Q^6)$, hence reducible.
5. If we introduce R, satisfying $R^3 + R^2 + 1 = 0$, we again get a field with 8 elements. An isomorphism can be established by making R correspond to Q^3, R^2 to Q^6, and so on. (There are also two other ways of establishing an isomorphism.) The R-field is thus the Q-field in disguise.
6. Q, Q^2, Q^4. Exponents are powers of 2. Note $Q^8 = Q$, $Q^{16} = Q^2$, $\cdots$

(PAGE 147)

1. $S = P + Q$, $T = Q - P$.
2. $P = \frac{1}{2}(S - T)$, $Q = \frac{1}{2}(S + T)$.
3. —.
4. (a) Yes. (b) Yes. (c) No. (i) fails. (d) No. (ii) fails.
5. (a) No. (i) fails. (b) No. (ii) fails.
6. U, V form basis if $ad - bc \neq 0$.

(PAGES 161–162)

1–5 ask for proofs.
6. (i) V.8. (ii) V.7 and V.9.

(PAGE 166)

1. Linearly independent.
2. Linearly dependent. $9A + B - 28C = 0$.
3. Linearly dependent. $A + B + C = 0$.
4. Linearly independent.

(PAGE 174)

Question. x, y, z.

(PAGE 177)

Answers different from those below are not necessarily wrong. A system can be reduced to standard form in many ways.

1. $x + y + z$; $y + z + t$; $z + t + u$.
2. $x + 2y + 3z + 4t$; $y + 2z + 3t$. $C = 2B - A$. $D = 3B - 2A$.
3. $x - 2y + z$, $y - z$. $C = -A - B$.
4. $x - y$, $y - z$. $C = -A - B$.
5. $x + y$, $y + z$, z.

(PAGE 194)

1. —.
2. They form a vector space of four dimensions. The equation is of the fourth degree.
3. They form a basis. $m^4 - 10m^2 + 1 = 0$. The roots of this equation are $\pm\sqrt{2} \pm\sqrt{3}$.
4. $1, r, r^2 \cdots r^{n-1}$ form basis. n dimensions. Degree n.

(PAGE 198)

Fourth degree. $x^4 - 10x^2 + 1 = 0$.

(PAGE 202)

1. 2.	4. 2.
2. Case (i).	5. 2.
3. 3.	6. 2, 3.

Index